EX LIBRIS

BEST
SELLERS

BEST
SELLERS

FROM READER'S DIGEST
CONDENSED BOOKS

THE READER'S DIGEST ASSOCIATION
Pleasantville, New York

CONTENTS

STILL
MISSING

ALEX SELKY, age 6
Last seen May 15, 1980, 8:50 a.m., corner of Fremont and Beacon
Wearing blue jeans, red and white T-shirt, blue running shoes
Persons with any information, call 966-3411

A condensation of the novel by **Beth Gutcheon**. Illustrated by Ted Lewin.

Alex Selky was six going on seven. He knew not to dawdle on the way to school, never to talk to strangers. He knew to come straight home afterward. He had done it many times. He was a big boy now. Then one morning, after waving good-by to his mother, Alex turned the corner—and disappeared.

Was he lost? Had he been kidnapped? Was he still alive? For Susan Selky, the torment was nearly unbearable. Others shared her anguish: her estranged husband, Graham; Detective Menetti, whose hunt for Alex became an obsession. Friends, even concerned strangers, took to the streets in a relentless search.

But as the days turned to weeks and Alex was still missing, it was Susan who never lost faith. Somehow, somewhere, she *knew* her child would be found alive and brought back to her.

You could hardly get to age thirty-four without learning something about loss. By thirty-four you're bound to have lost your Swiss army knife, your best friend from fourth grade, your chance to be center forward on the starting team, quite a few of your illusions, and certainly, somewhere along the line, some significant love. Susan Selky had in fact recently lost an old battle, for her marriage to the man she was in love with, and, with it, her dreams of more babies and of holding his hand in the dark when they were old.

It may be that one loss helps to prepare you for the next, but the truth is that life is not something you can go into training for. There was nothing that Susan Selky could have done to prepare for the breathtaking impact of losing her son.

Susan Selky, bright, loyal, stubborn, shy, accomplished. If you knew her professionally, you probably wouldn't have guessed that she thought of her narrow brick house on Fremont Street as if it were a shell, guarding the heart of her life, her private days and nights with Alex.

Alexander Graham Selky, Jr., age six and three quarters, a free-lance spaceman. A small, sturdy child with a two-hundred-watt smile and a giggle like falling water, a child who saw *Star Wars* once with Mommy, twice with Daddy, and once again with

TJ, the original owner-trainer of Taxi, an oversize Shetland sheepdog.

Taxi was a near total loss in the training department. He had only managed to learn to start barking with joy when Alex got home from school, a full minute before any human could have heard his feet on the stairs, and to smuggle himself soundlessly onto Alex's bed at night against orders. Most evenings when Susan went to kiss Alex one more time on her own way to bed, she found Taxi burrowed against her sleeping boy, still as a statue except for the wistful eyes that begged, Pretend you don't see me.

"He thinks he's my brother," said Alex. "He thinks he's a fur person."

Alex Selky, going on seven, so eager to grow up, kissed his mother good-by on their front steps on the hot, bright morning of Thursday, May 15, 1980, and marched himself down the street to the New Boston School of Back Bay, two blocks from his corner. He never arrived at school, and from the moment he turned the corner, he apparently disappeared from the face of the earth.

It was only two fifty in the afternoon when Susan jogged down Fremont Street. She'd been held up after her seminar by a chatty student, and she was worried that she wouldn't get home before Alex. The entryway in her house was dark; the tenant of her ground-floor apartment was at work. Alex's bike lay against the wall by the stairs that led up to the two floors Susan and her son occupied. As she unlocked her upstairs door, she could hear Taxi flinging himself against it on the other side, howling with delight that one of his people had come back.

Inside, Susan bent over him fondly. "Hush, lovely Taxi. Can't learn not to bark my ears off, can you, poor Taxi?"

She found her morning *Globe* and settled herself in a deep chair by the window. Sunlight flooded this front room in the afternoons, slanting in across the bright blue chairs and sofa, the fading Persian carpet, and the dark, wide polished floorboards. What a pleasure it was to have the room in ticking silence for a minute or two.

It was almost three thirty before something caused her to look at her watch. That was the moment it began. It was thirty minutes since school let out. It took seven minutes to walk home from the schoolyard. Where was Alex?

She went to the window and leaned out over the sidewalk. The street lay silent in the sunlight. She watched for a moment or two, knowing that if she refused that quiver of fear starting under her rib cage, Alex would sprint around the corner bouncing his green knapsack.

"I won't dawdle," he had said manfully when he asked permission to walk home alone from school. "You can *count* on me."

"Okay," she had said, reaching across the supper table to shake on it. Alex shook, and with his elbow overturned his milk.

Susan kept her eyes on the corner, trying to make Alex appear by force of will. Just do it. Just come around the corner, panting, with your cheeks flushed and your brown hair flying and your totally plausible six-year-old's explanation. Just show up right now, my good little man, before I allow this feeling to have a name, and panic, and make a fool of myself. (Yes, I know I said he was missing, Officer, but you see he was actually at his friend's house reading Batman comics. Yes, he *is* here now. He just . . . But you see, he promised he wouldn't dawdle. . . . Seven. Well, almost seven. But he's very responsible. Well, I'm sorry. Yes, I know I inconvenienced you. . . . No, I'm not a hysterical woman. I'm a tenured professor of American literature at Harvard. . . . I *said* I was sorry.)

The street was so strangely still that Susan went to the phone and called Jocelyn. "Hey," she said. "It's me."

"Hey. I'm glad you called. I'm really having a swell day, let me tell you. I waited four hours for the plumber to get here. I was late to pick up Justine and everything."

"Oh, Justine's home?" asked Susan.

"Finally. I had to stop and feed her on the way, though, because she traded her lunch at school for a Catwoman doll."

"Oh, good, okay. Actually Alex isn't home yet, and I was wondering would you just ask Justine if she remembers if he stayed to play ball in the yard or anything?"

"Alex isn't *home* yet?"

That was a bad moment. The moment when you have to admit to another mother that you don't know where your child is.

"Hold on a sec," said Jocelyn.

Susan could hear her calling Justine.

It took a long time. It took such a long time that while she was holding on, Susan died and went to hell and came back a soul in torment. It took such a long time that before Jocelyn picked up the phone again, Susan already knew.

"Susan, Justine says Alex wasn't in school today at all."

Later Susan actually remembered hearing a crash at that moment. She remembered the words accompanied by a noise as if a giant tree were being shattered by lightning. There was a bright lurid flash, too, like the kind of frightening light you see in a thundersquall just at twilight.

He didn't go home with a friend? He didn't stop to read comics? She was still reaching for reasons for him not being home yet. She couldn't begin to grasp the idea of him not getting to school at all.

"Susan," said Jocelyn, "I'm coming over. Call the police."

Call the police. *Call the police.*

In the quiet room, in the sunlight, Susan felt herself sink into a well of horror so great that it was all colors, all light and all darkness, scalding heat and killing cold. The sensation was beyond anything you could feel and not be seared along every nerve and cell, altered forever. But you couldn't feel that way long without it stopping your heart. By the time Susan picked up the phone again, she had passed through the first shock. She was certainly not a hysterical woman as she called the police.

She didn't know what precinct she lived in. She dialed 911. "Yes, it's an emergency. My son has disappeared."

"What address?"

"Fremont Street. Back Bay."

"That's the Fourth District. I'll connect you."

The phone was answered on the first ring. "Fourth District."

"Yes. Hello. I want to report a missing child."

"That's Juvenile. Hold on."

The line went numb, then came alive again. Another voice said, "Detective Menetti."

It shook her to have to begin a third time. "Yes, I want to report . . . This is Mrs. . . . My son is missing. He's six years old."

"Name," said the toneless voice on the other end.

"My name is Susan Selky; his name is Alexander."

"Your address, Mrs. Selky?"

"Sixty-three Fremont Street. That's between Marlborough and Beacon."

"You last saw your son . . . when?"

"At eight fifty this morning. I kissed him good-by and watched him to the corner. The school is only two more blocks."

"He was last seen at eight fifty *this morning?* Why did you wait so long to call us?"

"Oh, please . . ." she said very softly.

"Never mind. I'll be right there." Lieutenant Menetti hung up.

The doorbell rang. Jocelyn and Justine. Taxi greeted them fervently but was a little surprised. *They* weren't Alex. He did his best to welcome them anyway. Justine, in a white leotard and a red peasant skirt, looked grave and held her mother's hand.

"He never *came* to school today," Justine started explaining to Susan while still climbing the stairs. "I waited outside for him until the bell rang. He has my red pencil."

Far in the distance, Susan heard a siren. It whined louder and louder through the streets toward them until at last it pulled up at the front door with a threatening wail. Jocelyn held Susan's hand as they listened to the footsteps on the stairs.

Susan felt weirdly calm, as if she were outside her body, picturing the scene. There she was, standing at the top of the stairs, holding her door open. She was slim, tall, with fine dark hair and

Still Missing

light blue eyes. There she was in her bare feet; her sandals were by the chair where she had curled up with the paper an hour ago. There was Jocelyn, with her fashionably wild brown hair streaked with gray, looking bony in her ancient blue jeans and work shirt, but, as always, carefully made-up. Here were the two detectives. This one was big, dark, fifty, with a flushed face and creases around his mouth and eyes. Detective Menetti. This other one was younger. Pale. Heavy.

Detective Menetti introduced himself and the other officer and registered Jocelyn's and Justine's names. Susan told him again what she'd told him on the phone.

"He never got to school at *all*," Justine kept piping up. "I waited for him. I waited and waited."

Menetti said, "Tell me a little about him, Mrs. Selky."

She hesitated. How can you tell a little about your whole child? "He's very responsible," she said. "The school's only two blocks up Beacon Street." To one side, the second detective was watching her.

"Can you let me have a more complete description?" Menetti asked. He had his pad out and his pen poised.

"Oh. Yes. He's, um, he's almost seven years old; he has straight dark brown hair. He's very friendly and happy, and he loves soccer . . . and riddles."

"How tall is he, Mrs. Selky?"

"How . . . well . . . he comes to right here on me." Her arms curved outward, as if to embrace her missing boy.

"He's exactly Justine's height," said Jocelyn softly.

Menetti looked at Justine. "I have a seven-year-old myself," he said to her. "I bet you weigh, what, fifty-five pounds?"

"Alex is a pound or two lighter," said Jocelyn.

"Wearing?" They looked at Susan.

She took a deep breath. "Wearing. Blue jeans, red-and-white T-shirt, and blue running shoes. He was carrying a green knapsack on his back."

"Okay, got that. Mrs. Selky, is Alex the kind of kid who talks to strangers?"

Susan shook her head. "We went over that when we decided he could walk to school by himself. We talked about strangers and what they might say, and the ways Alex could handle it."

"Okay. Now, when you say 'we decided'—you mean you and Mr. Selky?"

"I mean Alex and me. Graham and I are separated."

A look passed between the two detectives. "And how long have you been separated, Mrs. Selky?"

"Three months."

"Uh-huh. And where is Mr. Selky living now?"

"In Cambridge." Then she asked tartly, "Do you want to know with whom?"

"It was a painful separation, then?"

"Painful? Of course it was painful— May I ask why this is important? Couldn't we be doing something?"

"In just a second. Just a second. You had a custody fight, did you, over Alex, when you separated?"

Susan shook her head impatiently. "No, nothing like that. Graham and I didn't separate to hurt each other; we were trying to *stop* hurting each other."

"I see. Mr. Selky sees Alex when he wants to, then?"

"All the time. They adore each other. Graham's a wonderful father." Her voice was starting to tremble.

"Could we have your husband's address, Mrs. Selky?"

She recited it, and both detectives wrote it down.

"Good. Got it." Menetti snapped his pad shut. "Now, listen, Mrs. Selky. I know you're feeling anxious right now, and I don't blame you. I'm going to radio from my car for some extra help, and we're going to cover the neighborhood here. I have seven kids of my own, and I'll lay you odds we'll have your rascal back here for you by bedtime."

He smiled at Susan, and she felt a sudden thaw of hope. Could he be right? Of course he could.

"We'll canvass the neighborhood," Menetti went on. "There must have been people going to work that time of day who saw him. You and Mrs. Norris here can help out, if you would."

"Anything," said Jocelyn. "You name it."

"You can start phoning the parents of Alex's classmates. Find out if any of them saw him, tell them that he's missing, and tell them what he was wearing. Ask them to pass it on."

"You got it," said Jocelyn. Susan, mute, just touched her on the arm. Then Jocelyn went to the kitchen phone.

"I'm going down to my radio," Menetti said to Susan. "Do you mind if Detective Sachs looks over the house?"

Susan shook her head.

"Good. Now, remember, kids do *not* disappear into thin air. Sometimes we can't *find* them for a while, but they do not just disappear. Can you remember that? Keep calm." Menetti went downstairs.

Detective Sachs put away his pad and came forward. "Before we go over the house, Mrs. Selky, do you have a good picture of Alex you can let us have?"

Susan put her hand to her mouth nervously. "The most recent is . . . six months old. . . . Children change so fast. Maybe Graham has some more recent ones. Oh, God, I've got to tell him." She started for the phone.

"Mrs. Selky, please hold off doing that for a while."

"Doing what?"

"Calling your husband. Or your relatives. No need to alarm them yet, and it will make our job easier if you delay that."

"Really? But you told us to call our friends."

"I know, but we prefer to do it this way."

"Oh," Susan said vaguely. She felt taut as a harp string, one quivering thread of gut, and she was easily distracted. She sat down. Stood up. Said, "I'll get the pictures."

Detective Sachs followed her; then he went methodically from room to room, showing particular interest in the bathrooms. He opened the hamper in Susan's bathroom and took everything out, socks, towels, and underwear. In Alex's he did the same thing. He opened doors, checked closets. He studied the pictures on the mantel in Susan's bedroom. "This your husband?" he asked, pointing to a dark-haired man in a smiling family group.

"No," said Susan. "That's his brother, Robert. The blond one is Graham. They're twins, but you'd never know it. Fraternal."

"Good-looking guy," said Detective Sachs. "Your husband."

"Yes," said Susan, snatching snapshots from her mirror frame. "These are Alex." She laid them on the mantelpiece beside a large picture of Alex at five, his head thrown back in the sunlight, laughing. There were snaps of Alex in his Camp Woonsocket T-shirt, with a balloon at his first-birthday party, Alex on Graham's shoulders on Boston Common.

Detective Sachs tapped the mantel with his hand. "Must be nice, a fire in the bedroom." He crouched down and peered up into the chimney. He opened the flue and closed it again. Then he stood and asked, "Do you have a laundry?"

"Yes. In the basement. It's this way."

As they trooped downstairs, Sachs asked about the tenant in the ground-floor apartment.

"She's a widow named Margaret Mayo," said Susan. "She works at the MIT library."

"Does she have children?"

"Two. Grown up. They live in California, I think."

"I'd like to look around her apartment, if I may."

Susan got the key, and Detective Sachs went all through Margaret Mayo's apartment, opening closets, checking under the beds, looking into the refrigerator and the oven.

When they were finished, they turned off the lights, locked the door, and went on down the stairs to the cellar. Susan followed Detective Sachs patiently, feeling hopeful and curious. She didn't ask herself what he was doing. She simply clung to the simplicity of minutes passing and somebody doing something.

Detective Sachs was very thorough in the basement. He looked in the washer and the dryer. He took out his flashlight and checked behind the machines. In one corner he opened a crate full of place mats, cheese boards, and fondue pots still in gift boxes. He examined them, then straightened, saying, "You have a lot of fondue pots."

"It was the year of the fondue pot, the year I got married."

"My wife loves fondue pots," said Sachs. "She enjoys eating things with those little forks."

"I bet your wife feels safer having you work in Juvenile than on the Bomb Squad or something," Susan offered.

"Oh, I'm not on Juvenile," Sachs said. "I'm on Homicide."

As THE afternoon light began to .deepen into evening in the corners of the living room, so did Susan's horror. It was past Alex's suppertime. His package of chicken breasts lay in the refrigerator. Jocelyn had called family after family, but no one she had spoken to had seen Alex from the moment he turned the corner onto Beacon Street. It was as if he had walked out of sight and out of this life.

Jocelyn had gone home at six to continue her telephoning, because Detective Menetti had decided that they should keep Susan's line clear in case of a ransom call. Now Susan wanted to call Graham. In three months she had only called him at his office at Boston University, never at his girl friend's.

As she was trying to make herself go to the phone and dial the number, to say to a girl on the other end, This is Graham's wife, the phone rang. It was very loud, and Susan jumped. Detective Menetti gestured to her to answer. Upstairs, she knew, another detective would silently pick up the extension.

Susan picked up the phone, said, "Hello," and started praying.

"Susan?" said a woman's voice, very young and low and tense. "This is . . . Naomi, Graham's friend."

Susan stopped praying. It took her a moment or two to whisper, "Oh."

"The police were just here, looking for Graham. They searched the apartment, and they kept asking me questions about Alex. They wouldn't answer any of my questions, but I suddenly felt so afraid for you. Susan . . . are you all right?"

Oh, please, thought Susan, don't let me cry.

She said, "Alex has disappeared, Naomi. He hasn't been seen since nine o'clock this morning. Where is Graham?"

"He . . . he told me he was having dinner with TJ, but I called there, and he isn't." Naomi paused, and Susan felt something in her heart go out to this younger one. "I would find Graham for you if I could," said Naomi simply. "I don't know what to say."

"It's all right. I know." Oh, I do know, she thought.

"Susan, could I tell you something?"

"Yes."

"I always wanted to tell you that I first introduced myself to Graham to tell him how I admired your study of Willa Cather."

Susan didn't answer. Her throat at that moment was aching with anger. She tried twice to speak again, but found she couldn't, so she just hung up.

Almost immediately the phone rang again. Menetti had to signal her twice to pick up the receiver.

"Susan. TJ. Look, did you know the police were looking for Graham?" His voice was big and deep. Susan pictured him, his tall, long-waisted body, in jeans with a hole nearly through his back pocket where he carried his keys. She began to cry.

"TJ, they're not looking for Graham; they're looking for Alex. He never got to school this morning, but I didn't know it, and he's been gone all this time. TJ, can you help me?"

"I'm on my way," he said, and the phone clicked down. TJ was Graham's closest friend and Alex's godfather. He was smart and wry and absolutely true. If you were facing the longest night of your life, TJ was the one you'd want to face it with.

By the clock it was less than eight minutes between the time she hung up and the moment she heard TJ's ancient Porsche screech to a stop in front of her house. He used his own front-door key and took the stairs three at a time, with his plump little girl friend, Annie, scampering behind him. Annie waited while TJ wrapped Susan in a long, speechless embrace. Susan kept a tight grip on his hand even as she then kissed Annie. With them in the room the blue glow of the last light outside the window seemed less evil.

21

After introductions, Detective Menetti questioned both TJ and Annie about Graham. They had no idea where he was.

"This is going to take him apart," said TJ. "He thinks Alex makes the sun rise."

"Can you help me find Graham, Mr. French?" asked Menetti.

"Dr. French," said Susan.

"TJ," said TJ. "Sure, I can help find Graham, but I'd rather find Alex. Have you got any leads at all yet?"

Menetti and Sachs exchanged glances. "We've got a lot of people who recognize the boy," said Menetti. The police on the street were now carrying copies of the photograph of Alex in his camp T-shirt. "We've got a dozen who know they see him most mornings, and we've got a couple who think they saw him today."

"What does that mean, they *think?*"

"Well, in a case like this, everyone wants to help, to turn in the big clue. Pretty soon they're positive they saw him this morning, only it turns out that they saw him last week."

"In other words, you don't have anyone who definitely saw him after he left Susan?"

"Not at this moment, no. But we'll check out every lead we get." Almost as if talking to himself, Menetti continued, "He could have wandered off and fallen down and gotten hurt and taken a while to come to. He could be in a hospital, and eventually he'll identify himself. If he doesn't, we'll see the report, an unidentified patient. Or he could be afraid you'd be mad at him for getting lost, so he doesn't want to come home."

Susan absorbed this picture. However wrenching the thought was, it was something to hope for. That her sweet, good boy, trying so hard to help, somehow (But how? *How?* Don't think about it. . . .) did in fact take a wrong turn trying to walk up Beacon Street to school, and that he didn't ask for directions because he'd been told not to talk to strangers, and that he felt more and more bewildered and embarrassed until finally he just sat down somewhere and decided to wait for help. It could be worse . . . there could be worse things. . . .

"And if he's not lost?" asked TJ.

"Well, there are other possibilities," said Menetti. "One is kidnapping. For money. Mrs. Selky tells me that her father is comfortable and Mr. Selky's parents are fairly wealthy. In other words, she could raise a ransom if she had to."

"But wouldn't a kidnapper go for some Rockefeller kid?"

"Listen," said Menetti. "Kidnapping isn't a crime for pros. Unless it's political, your kidnapper is probably on his maiden voyage, and he may do things that you and I would consider stupid. Like picking a kid whose family doesn't have big money. Also, there are plenty of people who would look at this house and this street, and to them that is big money. Kid in private school. Both parents professors. They might just have hung around and seen that here was a pretty small kid who always walked the same two blocks every morning, and just picked him because it would be easy."

Susan put her head in her hands. TJ went over and knelt in front of her chair and lifted her arms around his neck. "Don't think it," he said, holding her with both arms. "He *is* old enough to walk two blocks by himself. You didn't risk him; you gave him room to grow up, by trusting him."

"Room to grow up?" She wept, so softly that only TJ could hear. "This is very hard. . . ."

"Don't cry yet," TJ whispered. "It's not time for that. It's time to have faith." He felt her quiet herself.

Menetti said, "I'm finding it pretty hard to figure out how a kid could disappear so fast or completely unless he was taken into a building right near here, or into a car—"

The phone rang. Susan ran for it. It was Alex's teacher, distraught because she hadn't called Susan immediately when she learned that the school nurse hadn't received a call to explain Alex's absence. "I never *thought* . . ." The woman sobbed. "Parents often forget to call us when they keep a child home."

"It's all right," Susan kept murmuring to her. "It's all right. It's not your fault." What am I talking about? her head said while her mouth spoke. It's *not* all right.

When she came back to the living room, Menetti was saying,

"Something that happens more often than you think is a kid getting stolen by someone who just wants a kid. We've seen an increase in those cases since the abortion law was passed. There are less babies around now to adopt, and some people really want children."

"What kind of person *does* that?" asked TJ.

"You name it. Can be a lonely woman . . . or man . . . a frustrated grandparent. They sit around the park, they watch the kids, they hear the mothers complain. They start telling themselves young people aren't taking proper care of the kids, and the next thing you know they've adopted one, as a public service.

"We had a case last year of a teenage boy who stole a little two-year-old he'd been baby-sitting for. We picked them up in Texas after almost a month. The kid said he just felt like hitting the road, and he wanted a traveling companion.

"See, with that kind of situation, they just want the kid; they don't really think about what it's going to be like, how long you have to hide him, how you do it, where you go, what a kid needs."

TJ and Susan looked at each other, and TJ could almost hear her thinking that it sounded much more likely than some amateur ransom job—the idea that someone, some lonely person, could look at her lovely, jaunty little boy and just want him so badly, she took him.

"Of course," said Menetti, "it's a long shot that we're ever going to seriously face that kind of possibility."

"Why do you say that?" TJ asked.

Menetti frowned. "Look, you gotta understand. What is it—some sixty percent of murderers know their victims? Now, usually, when a child disappears, you've got a runaway or you've got custodial interference. You know."

"I *don't* know," said Susan, staring at him.

"Look," said Menetti. "You just separated from your husband, right? You're still pretty ticked off at him, right? And he's pretty ticked off at you. I know you say, 'Not my husband, *he'd* never do a thing like this,' but nine times out of ten, when a kid disappears, the person you look for first is the other parent."

"I am not ticked off at Graham!" said Susan sharply. "And he is not ticked off at me. Oh, God. You *can't* be doing all you can to find out what really happened if you're seriously wasting men on looking for Graham. I thought you were trying to reach him to tell him about Alex. I thought you just wanted to ask him for his help."

For the first time TJ, too, showed signs of his own anger. "Look, sir, you are way off the mark—"

The phone rang. Everyone froze. Susan picked it up. "Hello?"

"Hello," said a woman's voice. "Is this Mrs. Selky?"

"Yes, this is she." Susan had to push to make her voice come out at normal volume. Who are you? Do you have my son?

"Mrs. Selky, this is Maureen Laugherty with the Channel Eleven news team, and we understand that your six-year-old boy has vanished into thin air."

"Oh!" Susan wailed in frustration. "It's some woman from the news. . . ."

Menetti took the phone from her. "This is Detective Menetti," he said. "The situation is that the child is missing, and we have no more information whatsoever. There will be no more comment at this time." He hung up, then called up the stairs to the officer listening on the extension and told him to cut in on all press calls with the word that there was no comment at this time and that police orders were to keep the line clear.

"Okay," Menetti said to Susan. "Now we'll be in for it. I'm surprised we stayed clear this long, with my men in the neighborhood and your Mrs. Norris calling everyone in the city. I'm going to order a cordon in the street, so no one can get close to the house, but we can't keep the press from camping all up and down the block or from interviewing your neighbors. I'm afraid that with you and your husband both professors and Alex such an appealing kid, you're going to look like awfully good copy."

The phone rang again. Susan picked it up, but before she even spoke, the voice said, "This is 'News Center Four' calling," and she heard the officer upstairs take it, so she hung up.

Alex hungry and frightened. Alex out there in the dark, crying.

Alex in a hospital, unconscious, no identification for them to notify her. Alex threatened by criminals . . .

"I want to know where he is," Susan said to Menetti. "I want to go on TV. Whatever it is, wherever he is, I want everyone to see me, to know that I love him, and that I just want to know . . ."

Menetti looked surprised. "Are you sure?" he asked. "Do you know what it's going to be like to face the media? It's not Walter Cronkite out there. It's some very ruthless garbage hounds."

She shrugged. "Doesn't matter. Couldn't hurt any more. It's the one thing I can do."

The phone rang again. Again, the caller introduced herself; it was Vivienne Grant with Channel 5 News. She wanted to know if she could do a live interview with Susan, in the missing boy's bedroom. "Yes," said Susan. "Yes, you can."

The phone rang again. It was Jocelyn. "How are you, baby?" she murmured. "Is there anything new at all?" Susan said not. "Well, I've got Katherine Abbot and Martina Rolley calling, too. I think we've reached every parent from Beacon Hill to Porter Square. People are praying for you. I've got a whole army out here ready to help, if there's anything they can do."

"Thank you, Jocelyn. Thanks for what you've done already. Just a minute, Detective Menetti wants to talk to you."

Susan listened to Menetti saying, "Mrs. Selky wants to go public . . . the eleven-o'clock news. It may be that we'll flush something out pretty quickly. If nothing happens, if you've really got some volunteers lined up, let's have a meeting with them right here at ten tomorrow morning. Can you get that word out? Okay. Yes, she's all right; she has some friends here. . . . No, we're still looking for Mr. Selky. . . . Yes. Good-by."

As he hung up, Annie went to answer a light tapping at the door, and came back, followed by Margaret Mayo, Susan's tenant. She was a graceful sixty-year-old woman with iron-gray hair and brilliant eyes and one of the world's readiest smiles. She somehow introduced herself to everyone in the room while moving straight to Susan. She took her hand and gave her a strong, steady gaze. "I want to know how I can help you."

"Margaret, thank you. I don't know. There doesn't seem to be anything we can do."

"Well, tell me this, have you called your father?"

Susan looked at her.

"You were hoping any moment Alex would be found, and *then* you could let him know you'd had a scare."

Susan nodded.

"But you can't just let him hear it on the news," said Margaret. "Why don't I call him for you? I'll call Graham's parents, too. Where are the numbers?"

Susan pointed to the list in felt-tip pen on the wall above the telephone. "Margaret, thank you." It was all in her voice—she so much didn't want to make those calls.

"You're welcome," said Margaret. "First, would you like a big hug?" Susan actually smiled for the first time in hours. Margaret's hug was warm and firm and deliberate. Susan hadn't felt that particular brand of comfort since her mother died.

Menetti thanked Margaret, too, and asked her to make the calls downstairs, from her own phone. "Certainly," said Margaret. "In fact, why don't you always use my phone for making calls out? That way you can keep this number free."

The phone rang twenty-two times in the next hour. It was getting on toward eleven. Some of the callers were friends wanting news. The other calls were from news personnel. Reporters and camera crews had now gathered outside. Huge lights illuminated the façade of the house, and the sidewalk was a snake's nest of cables from lights and microphones. Presently an officer in charge of the press chose a small group to come inside for the live interview.

Susan felt numb as technicians tested connections and the lighting men ran up and down the steps. She could hardly think of Alex. There was so much confusion that she was finding it hard to recapture some concrete detail of him. The smell of his hair warm from the sun. The perfect roundness of his head, how it fitted the curve of her palm when she stroked it. A woman with a large black case kept asking her something she couldn't understand. Finally Margaret Mayo intervened. "No, she doesn't want any makeup," she said gently. "She feels like hell, and she might as well look that way."

Vivienne Grant wanted Susan sitting on Alex's bed, holding something that belonged to him. "Get the dog in the shot," the cameraman kept urging. Taxi, thought Susan with a stab of worry. Had anyone fed him this evening? Taxi came into the bedroom and lay down by her feet, looking bewildered, but got up and ran out of the room as they switched on the brilliant lights. "Damn," said the cameraman. "Can you call him back?"

"No," Susan said. "It's too bright."

"Well, could you hold something of the boy's, then? How about a teddy bear?" Susan looked at the threadbare plush rabbit that was lying, as always, on Alex's pillow.

"No," she said. "I think not." She felt strangely calm. Now Alex's room was a movie set. Alex was nowhere. Alex had been gone for years. There had never been a real Alex.

Suddenly Vivienne Grant began to speak, looking intently into the camera. "We're here on

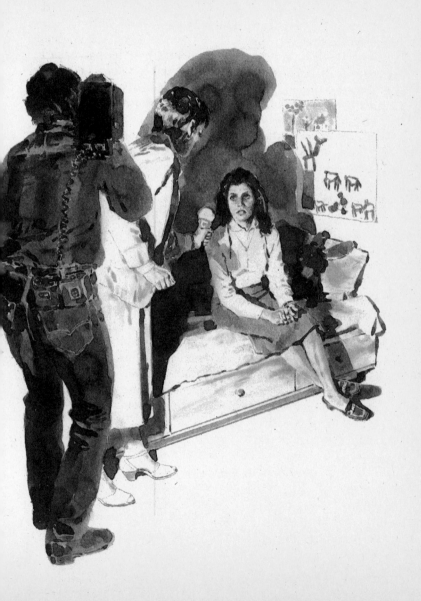

Fremont Street at the home of Mrs. Susan Selky, where today, tragedy struck. Mrs. Selky's little son, Alex, whom you see in this photograph, left for school this morning at eight fifty as usual. Although the boy is only six, we're told he is an unusually responsible child, and for several months now he has been allowed to walk to school by himself. But this morning, somewhere between the corner of Beacon and Fremont streets and the New Boston School, two blocks away, Alex disappeared. Mrs. Selky, could you tell us, please, exactly what happened?" She stepped slightly sideways so the camera could move in on Susan.

Susan's voice was clear and calm. "Alex left the house at eight fifty this morning. He was wearing blue jeans, a red-and-white striped T-shirt, and blue running shoes; he was carrying a green knapsack. I watched him walk to the corner, and he turned and waved to me." He waved to me! I forgot that, until this second! "Then he turned the corner," Susan's calm voice continued, "and disappeared. He never reached school."

"I see," said Vivienne Grant. "Tell me, Mrs. Selky, would Alex have been on his guard against strangers?"

Of course Alex was on his guard against strangers. Of *course* he understood that there were people in the world not to trust or talk to. And don't say again that he was "only six." He's known since he was two that traffic could kill him, and he certainly knew not to wander off with a stranger offering lollipops.

"He is friendly but wise," Susan said, "and he was very proud of being trusted to walk by himself. He doesn't dawdle and he doesn't wander. I would like to appeal to your audience. . . . Please," she said straight to the camera, "if you have any information about Alex, please get in touch with the police."

Vivienne Grant stepped back into the shot. "In Boston tonight, a mother's nightmare. Alex Selky, missing at age six. His mother, a professor of literature at Harvard, is showing a great deal of courage. The boy's father, Graham Selky, teaches English at Boston University; he has been separated from his wife for three months. Police are looking for Mr. Selky, but they say that he is not officially a suspect. This is Vivienne Grant, in Back Bay."

The moment the scene was finished, Susan shot up from where she was sitting and made her way through the equipment back to Menetti. He was on the phone, confirming a special police number for viewers to call, to be broadcast before the end of the program. He said, "Right—got it," then hung up. Menetti was beginning to look haggard, and the thought occurred to Susan that he wasn't just doing a job—he really cared about Alex.

"Detective Menetti . . ." she said.

"Look, why don't you call me Al?" he said to her wearily.

"Al, I know you don't have all the men in the world. Will you *please, please* not waste time chasing Graham. We may have had problems, but this isn't a crazy family. We're normal people, and some lunatic has done something . . . to our . . ." She could feel the hysteria welling up in her chest.

"I know how you feel," Menetti began.

"No, you don't. Excuse me, but you cannot possibly know at this moment how I—" The phone rang.

"Susan?" said the anxious voice. "This is Robert."

"Robert!" Graham's brother? Detective Menetti asked her soundlessly. She nodded yes.

"I'm in Boston. I just saw you on the news. Susan, is there anything I can do?"

"But you're never in Boston. What are you doing here?"

"I came up last night. I can't believe this is happening. Where is Graham?"

"Robert, we don't know where he is, really."

"I'm coming right over there," said Robert.

"Okay," said Susan. She hung up.

"Robert's in Boston?" asked TJ. "That's weird."

"It *is* weird," said Susan.

"Robert's one of those types who brags about never stepping in the provinces except to change planes," TJ explained to Annie.

There was some kind of commotion downstairs, an increasing murmur of raised voices. Then one voice soared to desperate volume. "Just get the hell out of my way. *I want my wife!*"

"Graham!" TJ and Susan cried at the same time.

31

Menetti threw open the door and yelled down, "Let him up!"

In another moment Graham burst through the door. The expression on his face was something Susan felt she'd never forget for the rest of her life. She ran to him and held him as hard as she could, knowing that the first shock was burning through his heart and mind like acid, as if it would literally kill him.

"I was in a taxi," he said into her hair. "The driver had the news on the radio." His voice sounded as if he were strangling. Susan felt his anguish as he tried not to cry.

TJ put his hand on Graham's shoulder, then wrapped an arm around him and clasped him hard.

Graham gave TJ his hand. "Thank you for being here, man," he said. "Annie"—over TJ's shoulder—"thank you for coming." The two men looked very alike, both tall and muscular, but Graham had thick honey-blond hair. He wore a dark blue shirt and a tweed jacket, and looked almost exactly the same as when Susan had fallen in love with him twelve years ago. Except that his eyes no longer glowed with that generous joy that he had back when he was young and thought he couldn't lose. That didn't stop Susan from feeling a surprised burst of love at the tilt of his head and the swing of his hips every time she saw him.

Tonight his eyes were dull with fear. She could feel him staring around, as she had for hours, unable to believe that Alex wasn't in the next room. Soon he would feel the numbness begin. Soon he would be with her in the unreality.

"Mr. Selky," said Menetti firmly, "could you please tell me where you have been for the last six hours?"

Graham made a face as if he couldn't answer. "All this time," he said, and his arms went around Susan, "all this time, and I could have been here and *done* something. . . ."

"Mr. Selky? I really must know," Menetti pressed.

"I was visiting a friend." Graham didn't look at him.

"Mr. Selky," said Menetti, "I have had police officers who could have been otherwise occupied looking for you for six hours, and I want to know *exactly*—"

"I was in Charlestown trying to seduce a nurse!" Graham

yelled. "Do you want to talk to her? You'll find it delightful; she's got a vocabulary of at least forty words." Then he did begin to cry, and Susan, stricken for him, held his bowed head against her cheek and began to cry, too.

"I'm afraid I will have to talk to her," said Menetti.

Graham shook Susan off and covered his face with his hands, furiously stripping away the tears. Then he began searching his pockets, which, she knew, were always an owl's nest of receipts, deposit slips, and scraps of paper with phone numbers. Suddenly he threw them all on the floor. "I don't have her number. What the hell does it matter? *Where is my son?*"

"Hey, Graham," said TJ. "Cool down. Menetti's only trying to do his job."

"So why isn't he out doing it?"

"He's asking you where you were because they thought you might have taken Alex."

"They thought what?"

"Look," said TJ, "they don't know you. You've got to let them check out your story so they'll believe you."

Graham groaned. "I met her on a bus. Her name is Claire. She works at Mount Auburn Hospital. That's all I know."

TJ stared at him. "If I didn't feel so frightened for you right now, I'd wring your neck, man."

"Please," said Graham. "Please."

"Call Naomi," said TJ.

Graham looked at Susan. "She called me," said Susan. "The police were at her apartment looking for you—and for Alex. She was very worried."

"Okay. I'll call her."

"You can use Mrs. Mayo's phone downstairs," said Menetti. "We're keeping this line clear."

After Graham, followed by a policeman, had gone out the door, Robert arrived. Menetti watched him closely as he greeted Susan and TJ and was introduced to Annie. Smaller, darker, with something soft about him, he looked nothing like his brother, and yet he had a kind of presence. Perhaps it was his self-absorption,

Menetti thought; but there was something about him that seemed not precisely restful.

"Susan, it's *unreal*," Robert kept saying. He was right about that, so Susan nodded. Just then Graham returned, and Robert cried, "Graham, I can't believe it!" They shook hands.

"Robert. It's strange to see you in Boston."

"Well, it was last minute; someone got sick, and I was asked to fill in at a conference on public broadcasting."

Graham seemed to tune him out, saying to Menetti, "There must be something we can do besides standing here. Couldn't TJ and I take the dog or something and go out there?"

"I had a team of trained men on the street for as long as we had light," said Menetti. "There just isn't anything to see now."

"I want to help. I want to do something."

"I think you're going to have to help each other get through tonight," said Menetti.

"Are you going to stay?" Susan asked the detective. She realized she was beginning to have problems with time; she wasn't sure if it was midnight or four in the morning.

"Yeah," said Menetti. "I guess I'd have to say the odds are with ransom now. If we're going to hear from the kidnappers, my guess is the first contact will come in the next six hours."

"What about hospitals?" Graham asked suddenly. "Did you think of that? Supposing he's hurt and unconscious and—"

"We've checked them all," said Menetti. "Nothing."

"Oh," said Graham.

For the first two hours after the news broadcast the phone seemed to ring every time it touched the cradle. Susan's father called; Graham's parents called. Students and colleagues of Graham's and Susan's called; total strangers called, offering help. Others called to offer psychic information and tips from God.

Margaret took all the calls, while an officer listened in upstairs. Menetti thought it would be best, psychologically, for a woman to answer a ransom call. Susan's frantic jittery feeling had worn off, and she felt muffled and numb again. She just wanted to sit

34

still and try to make her mind remember what had happened. The major fact kept escaping her, like a dream in which you know you're in prison for life but can't remember why.

She would suddenly have a vivid picture of Alex still and white. An arm broken and bent the wrong way. Dry brown blood at his nose and mouth. His eyes were open, glazed in an expression of horror, the first knowledge of terror, coming into his life at the moment it ended.

After three a.m. the phone calls began to taper off. For Graham's benefit and Robert's, Menetti went over the possibilities again. Alex might be lost and for some reason be afraid or ashamed to ask for help. . . .

"But he knows to look for policemen," said Graham. "And he knows his phone number, and he always carries a dime."

"How would he reach a phone in a phone booth?" asked Robert. "A little kid, he couldn't reach the dial."

"He would ask someone to lift him up," said Susan. "Or to dial for him." But she was picturing big hands picking Alex up. Big hands, grasping and crushing.

"He could have asked the wrong person for help," said Robert. "We've got to face it."

We? thought Susan. Suddenly she wished Robert would go away. She started to cry.

Quite a while passed in silence. Annie, sitting with TJ in one big chair, settled her head on his shoulder and fell asleep. Graham and Susan sat side by side on the couch. Graham held Susan's hand. Margaret sat at the table by the telephone, playing solitaire. Menetti, in the chair by the window, slept sitting bolt upright. TJ fell asleep. Robert got up eventually and went up the stairs. From the creaking on the floor above as he walked, Susan knew he'd gone into Alex's room and stretched out on the bed.

In the darkest hours of the night Susan thought, If it's kidnap, if it's ransom, then he's not dead. If he's not dead, then the phone will ring. What I must do is make the phone ring. People say you can make something happen by making an image of it happening. So I am picturing the phone ringing, right now. I am hearing the

35

voice on the other end. "Hello, Mrs. Selky?" or "Hello, Mommy?"

I am picturing the phone beginning to ring. In the next second it is going to ring. I can feel it; you sometimes hear it a second before it actually starts to ring.

They sat in that room like stones, until the gray morning light started leaking in like the death of hope.

TJ and Annie woke up. Menetti went into the kitchen and made instant coffee. Margaret put away her cards and folded her hands in her lap. Graham stood up and began to pace around the room.

Menetti said, "Now that it's light again, we can do something."

"What?" asked Graham.

"We can get out there, and we can find every human being who was on the street yesterday morning."

Robert came downstairs, grunted hello at everyone, and went into the kitchen for coffee. Menetti stood staring down at the street. Suddenly he turned to Graham and said, "Well, I'll tell you this. A kid cannot disappear into thin air. Especially at eight fifty in the morning. Another thing, it's easier to hide a live kid than a dead one."

Susan came up behind them. "What did you say?"

"I said it's easier to hide a live kid than a dead one. A body is a real problem, especially in hot weather."

"He has a very small body," said Susan.

Graham put his arms around her. She leaned against him and closed her eyes. Everything went away for her except touch and sound. Warm, dark. Shirt against her cheek. Sound of someone—Robert—going up the stairs. Footsteps. Faint hiss. The shower.

It was hardly past first light when the phone rang in Jocelyn's darkened bedroom on Marlborough Street.

"Hi, it's Martina. I'm sorry, did I wake you?"

"Who could sleep?" Jocelyn answered groggily.

"I couldn't," said Martina. "I got up and went running. I kept thinking he's *out* there. I wondered if you'd heard anything."

"Not since about three thirty this morning. Susan was too wrecked to come to the phone, but her tenant, Margaret, said they hadn't heard a thing."

"Did you see Susan on the news? She was incredible."

"No, I didn't. I heard about it. I was still on the phone, but everyone said she was totally calm."

"She was incredible. My little boy has been stolen and he's probably been raped and murdered, and I'm not going to fall apart as long as there's a single thing I can do to help him. It was like that. If it were me, I'd have been on there *screaming*."

"No, you wouldn't," said Jocelyn. "You think you would, but when it's happening to you . . ."

"She had dignity. She was like that all through that mess with Graham, too. So in love with him and so angry and sad, but she was always fair. She just kept saying, you know, that it had been hard for Graham to feel stalled on that book he's been trying to write and to have people make such a fuss about *her* book."

"Did you hear they couldn't even find Graham until eleven thirty last night?" asked Jocelyn.

"I know," said Martina. "It must have been killing her. Well, I ought to call Susan now. I'm sure they're up."

"Yes. Look, Menetti's holding a meeting of volunteers at ten o'clock. Help get the word around, will you?"

"Right. It was good of you to do all that phoning yesterday," said Martina.

"Oh, it's not just about Alex, you know. If there's a pervert kid killer out there, it's about all of us with children."

"I know," said Martina.

WHEN the first editions of the Boston *Globe* and the *Record American* hit the morning streets, they carried the story of Alex's disappearance on page one. The *Record American* ran a front-page picture of his laughing face. The three national networks carried the story on their morning news broadcasts. About eighteen million people heard of Alex's disappearance over breakfast.

When Al Menetti walked into his kitchen in Saugus, his wife, Pat, had the "Today" show on. Eugene, Eileen, and Roberta were watching it while they ate. "Hi, Dad," they all mumbled.

Al's wife kissed him hello. She noticed his ashen face and gave him a look, but he turned to give his small children a hug and a kiss each in turn. Then he went upstairs to shower, shave, and change. From the bathroom window, he watched the three children walk to the corner to meet the school bus. Eugene lagged far behind the others, swinging his book bag. Al could tell from the little skips he took that Eugene was singing to himself.

Pat poured him a cup of coffee when he came downstairs. She made toast and brought it to him, then sat down with a cup of coffee for herself.

"See the news?" he asked her.

She nodded. "They had a picture of the little boy on."

"He's a few months younger than Eugene," said Al. "I saw these drawings he did, all taped to his wall. They look just like Eugene's." He stared into his coffee cup.

"How's the mother?" Pat Menetti asked. She was wearing blue jeans and one of her husband's shirts with the tail out. Al had a pure moment of seeing her suddenly not as the woman who kept serving frozen codfish cakes and who fell asleep in the movies, but as the pretty girl who met him when he was seventeen and never knew she would raise his seven children.

"The mother's good," he said thoughtfully. "She's amazingly good." He stared into space for a while, then spoke again. "I made a mistake last night. I put a lot of men on finding the separated father. Should have been able to tell from the mother that it wasn't a custody thing. She told me it wasn't, and it wasn't. I should have had the bloodhounds on the job right away. There's not much point now. They can't do much after eight hours."

"The thing I wonder," said his wife, "is, if you only have one child, and something happens to him, it must be the worst thing in the world. But then, when you have seven, don't you just worry for them seven times as much?"

"If you don't know, who does?"

"*I* don't know," said Pat. "But I don't see how she went on television like that. I couldn't have done it."

"Yeah, you could," he said, looking at her. "If you believed you could help Eugene, I bet you could."

"Are you sure there's nothing funny about her?" his wife asked.

"What do you mean?"

"She was so cool," said Pat.

Uh-huh, thought Menetti. Now it starts. Pat is thinking, It can't happen to me. That mother lost her kid, but if there's something funny about her, then there's a reason it could happen to her but it couldn't happen to me.

"There's nothing funny about her," Menetti said. He finished his coffee and stood up regretfully. "I have to be back in the city at ten. The Selkys have some volunteers, neighborhood parents and friends, coming in to see what they can do. I'll start them putting pictures of the kid around. After that, if anything's moving, I'll stay. Otherwise, I'll come home for dinner."

"Roberta's slumber party is tonight," Pat said.

"Good," he said wearily. "We can all sit around the TV with curlers in our hair."

WHEN Susan was growing up in Quaker Village, Ohio, a suburb of Cleveland, she thought of Boston as a place where people lived wider, richer lives than in Ohio. The Boston of her mind's eye with its Public Garden and the elegant sweep of Commonwealth Avenue seemed like a European capital. It was a place for people of character and wit, people who acted on principle.

By the time Susan and Graham moved to Boston, the city's first families had gradually sifted out of Beacon Hill and Back Bay to the rural comfort of the suburbs. The flavor and charm of the city neighborhoods had changed. Vast mansions along Commonwealth and Beacon had been converted to offices and schools. When Susan and Graham found their narrow town house on Fremont Street in Back Bay, it had been badly used by generations of students from the scattered institutions that Graham called collectively Unknown Junior College. It had taken the

Selkys seven years to fix up the house again, and it still had two unconverted rooms in the attic and was a little short on furniture. But for neighbors they had a Chinese scholar from Peking, a poet who worked for the *Atlantic Monthly*, and a curator from the Boston Museum of Fine Arts.

With one of the highest per capita student populations in the world, Boston seemed simultaneously very young and very old, a city full of diversity, experiment, tradition, and transience. To Susan it felt like a feast. There was a high-caste Hindu teaching assistant in her department, and a Boston Brahmin in Alex's play group, and her kitchen shelves were built by a carpenter from the South End who had a Ph.D. in philosophy. The South End, just across Copley Square from Back Bay, was a neighborhood in the midst of what Boston called gentrification. Row houses that had fallen into ruin were being restored by a mixture of young professionals, academics, and artists. The Fourth District police headquarters was on one seedy edge of the South End.

Menetti, driving in from the suburb of Saugus, had to remind himself that it takes all kinds. He'd worked his butt off to move out of Boston and to raise his kids in a place where everybody tried hard to stay married and keep the lawn cut. A city to him wasn't a place for people, especially kids. There was no center there. People moving in all the time, other people moving out. A city to him was more like a big zoo with cement floors and all the cage doors left open.

When Menetti arrived at the Selky house for his briefing of the volunteers, he was surprised to find more than a hundred people crowded into the living room, quietly waiting for him.

Susan saw him and rose from the chair where she had perched on the arm, leaning on Jocelyn. She couldn't seem to light anywhere for long; she had felt terribly restless and bereft while Menetti was gone. "They're being wonderful," she said to Menetti, gesturing around the jammed room.

Menetti surveyed the group. There were women in peasant dresses; there were women in jeans; there were slender women with delicate necks who looked like dancers. There were several men among the women. One was a well-known chef who lived in the South End with his lawyer wife. Another turned out to be a jazz clarinetist Menetti had admired since Police Academy days.

Graham stood and faced the room, clearing his throat for attention. "I want to thank you all for coming today. It means a great deal to Susan and me. Now I know you must have questions, so Lieutenant Menetti will try to answer them."

Menetti moved to the center of the room. What people wanted to know was whether their own children were in danger. There was a darting, stricken look in the eyes of the mothers.

"Do you have any idea," asked one woman, "if this was a crime committed by somebody Alex knew?"

"Well, we don't know yet that a crime was committed at all," said Menetti. "The boy may be lost."

"Are you saying that's what you think?" asked another mother.

"No, I'm not. I'm saying we don't know yet what's happened." A hundred attentive pairs of eyes were fixed on him. "We have leads. We're not in the dark. I don't want to be more specific, because of the press. But at this point, I want to make clear, our department has *never* had a case of a child this young disappearing without a trace."

"Lieutenant Menetti," asked Susan's friend Martina, "if you were raising a young child in this neighborhood, what would you go home and tell him? How would you handle this?"

Menetti had been waiting for this question. "Well," he said, "I'd have a talk with him about strangers, if you haven't already. But I also would supervise him pretty carefully."

"Meaning?" "What do you mean?" a dozen voices asked.

"Meaning, I don't think for the time being I'd let a young child out of the house without an adult."

"What do you mean by young?"

"I'd say . . . under twelve."

There was something awful in hearing him say something so specific. Why twelve? Why not eight? No one asked. Instead, Graham said, "Lieutenant Menetti, a lot of us would feel better if we could help."

"Absolutely," said Menetti. An officer who was waiting at the door came forward now with a stack of handbills. Menetti held one up. It showed two snapshots of Alex, one of his smiling face and the camp T-shirt, the other of him standing on the grass, holding a baseball cap and a mitt. Under the pictures was a description of what Alex was wearing, his age, and the exact time and place of his disappearance. Across the top of the paper was the bold headline MISSING.

Menetti asked them all to take handbills everywhere they went in the next few days. To staple them onto trees, tape them onto lampposts. To get permission from every shop they could to post the handbills in the windows.

"Somewhere, somebody knows something," he said. "Somebody's seen something. If anyone gives you information directly, please write it down and get the source's name and address. Call the number on the handbill with anything you get, day or night. And . . . I think it will help to move fast."

As the volunteers left, Susan thanked each one for coming. She stood at the door, as if it were a receiving line. Some kissed her or touched her cheek as they passed. "It's remarkable how kind people are, really," she said when they were gone. She mused on the strangeness of this, the sense of community. Then she drifted into trying to picture Alex. Trying to bring back a round, scented image of him, of his touch. All she could see was his photograph on the poster. MISSING. Yes.

By sundown it seemed that there were posters of Alex in every drugstore, butcher shop, luncheonette, and boutique from the Charles River to Boston Harbor. The six-o'clock news on all stations carried interviews with volunteers. "Mrs. Norris, you've been walking for two hours now, putting up handbills of the missing boy, Alex Selky. Why are you doing that? . . . I see, and are you worried for your own child? . . . I see. . . . From Boston, the scene of a truly stirring volunteer effort to find little Alex Selky, missing now for thirty-three hours. This is Vivienne Grant . . ."

There was an interview with Susan, too, taped early in the afternoon. "We're very grateful to the community for their help and support," she said calmly. "My husband and I feel very hopeful that something or someone will lead us to Alex very quickly."

"You believe, then, that your son is alive, Mrs. Selky?"

"Absolutely," she said to the camera.

Susan sat on her bed in the dusk, watching the broadcast, and wondered, How could I? How did I ever stand so straight and speak like that?

In Saugus, Detective Menetti turned off the news and got up to refill his glass. Roberta and her friends were in the kitchen making fudge. Eugene was listening to records upstairs.

"You look like you've been worked over by Nick the Bouncer," said Pat, glancing up from her needlepoint.

"I hate this case," he said.

"Do you think you're going to get an early break?" asked Pat.

He ignored the question. "You should hear the kinds of leads we have. A neighbor near the school is *sure* he saw the boy yesterday afternoon, unless it was the day before. A woman claims she saw him alone at ten a.m. walking on Newbury Street. She can't explain why she didn't think anything about it, a kid that age wandering around by himself during school hours.

"A man living on Beacon Street, around the corner from the Selky house, claims he saw a woman waiting in a car for about ten minutes the morning in question. He cannot describe the woman; he can sort of describe the car. But he never saw Alex; he just saw this car, and when he finished shaving and went downstairs at nine o'clock, it was gone. Then I've got a guy who thinks he saw Alex in a Cambridge food store at noon. He thinks he was with a punk with bad skin and peroxide hair. Now, why would a smart little kid who knew not to talk to strangers be pricing Twinkies with some pimply jerk instead of screaming his head off? Tell me the truth, would Eugene do that?"

Pat nodded over her needlepoint and went on working.

"I'm serious," said Menetti. "Is there anything some geek could say to Eugene that would get him to wander off shopping with him? Think about it. I want to know."

43

Pat thought about it. She shrugged. "If he promised to take him to meet the real Batman?"

"I hope you're kidding."

"I don't know if I am or not."

"Pat, what exactly have you told Eugene about strangers?"

"I've told him not to talk to them. I've told him not to go anywhere with them."

"Still, do you think some guy could talk Eugene into going with him, even though you've warned him about strangers?"

"Al, Eugene is seven years old. A seven-year-old is not a responsible person, no matter what you tell him. Not if he has to handle something that hasn't come up before. Sure, I think a reasonably bright grown-up could talk him into anything."

"I'll tell you where Alex Selky is," Menetti said suddenly. "His neighborhood is one block from the Esplanade, and these hot mornings the riverbank is full of people from sunrise on. Drunks, creeps, perverts . . . the whole mixed grill."

"Meaning?"

"Meaning, he was a beautiful little boy. Real beautiful, with a great smile. If he's not dead by now . . . It would probably be better if he was." As Menetti said that, tears came into his eyes.

Pat studied him from her chair, her hand over her mouth. "Do you want dinner?" she said at last. The sounds from the kitchen suggested that Roberta and her friends had reached the pot- and spoon-licking stage.

He wiped his eyes. "No . . . bed," he said.

AT MIDNIGHT the street was gleaming with a slow, cold, steady rain. Susan stood at her bedroom window, looking down. Alex, are you out in this? Alex, my baby, I know it's May, but won't you take your jacket? Alex . . . The gooseflesh on your arms when you're cold. O Lord, deliver me. Christ, deliver me. O God, help me. How do I bear unbearable loss?

In the church in which Susan was raised, there is a moment in the service when the choir rises and slowly marches down the center aisle, chanting. The rector walks behind them. He chants,

"O God the Son, Redeemer of the world"; and the choir and congregation respond, *"Have mercy upon us."* He chants, "From lightning and tempest; . . . from plague, pestilence, and famine; from battle and murder, and from sudden death," and the people respond, *"Good Lord, deliver us."* It is the Litany, the oldest chant in the prayer book, and tonight it was reverberating in Susan, a primitive longing for ritual.

Downstairs in the living room, the bright blue couch had been pushed against the wall to make room for a long table the police had brought in. There were now three telephones on it, Susan's and the special police phone with an extension. Three uniformed officers sat at the table in a row, smoking cigarettes and drinking coffee from paper cups, logging in every telephone call. The phones seemed to ring incessantly. There had been nearly four hundred calls between noon and midnight.

By midafternoon Menetti had had more than three hundred uniformed officers in the streets, searching every house and store and garage and warehouse. Helicopters cruised overhead, scanning rooftops and piers, looking for a place a small boy could have ventured out and become stuck or trapped. Blue-and-white patrol cars drove slowly through the streets, broadcasting through PA systems on the car roofs. "We are looking for a white male child, age six. He is wearing a red-and-white striped T-shirt, blue jeans, and blue running shoes. His name is Alex. Anyone with information concerning this child, please call the police."

Menetti was downstairs most of the time keeping in touch with searchers through a communications van parked in front of the house. Graham and TJ were out in the streets all day, going everywhere Alex would go, doing everything Alex did. Two blue-coated policemen followed them, taking notes, asking questions. They reported to Menetti on walkie-talkies every ten minutes. Nothing so far. Nothing yet. Nothing.

By dinnertime neighbors had dropped off homemade bread and casseroles at the house. Susan tried hard to swallow some soup Margaret prepared, but she only felt nausea boil up in her.

"I can't eat," Susan said, putting down her spoon.

Margaret understood. "I can't always eat. We'll try later."

The police were eating Big Macs at their table and continued to take phone calls while they chewed. The room seemed to be filled with racket. All evening the phones rang and rang, and it was torture. Then they began to ring less, and that was worse.

Susan had to wait until very late that night before she could say to herself, I was wrong to let him walk by himself. I was wrong. He was so young . . . too young. It was me.

There had been plenty of calls like that. The police didn't say so, but she knew. A six-year-old child wandering down the street by himself? What do you expect?

Susan sat in the darkness, feeling like an open wound.

She thought, It's days since I had any sleep. I should sleep, or else I'm going to hallucinate. This is much worse than last night. I can't even trace for myself what has happened in a clear linear way. Maybe I can be in the past again. I can be together in time with Alex, before . . .

The phone might ring. It could ring anytime. Couldn't it?

It's been fifteen years since I went to church. I stopped going because religion was the opiate of the masses. Tonight I see that faith isn't a drug. It's an active practice, an act of will. *Now* I see.

To have faith that Alex is alive—it has nothing to do with belief, or thought. Do I think he's alive? I commit myself to his being alive, as an act of will.

Lord, I believe; help thou mine unbelief.

I'm beginning to have longer stretches of my mind going blank. I think I'm beginning to slow down. I wonder if I could sleep.

SATURDAY morning, seven o'clock. It had been full light for over an hour. Hundreds of uniformed police were still carrying on their house-to-house search across Back Bay. Menetti had been downstairs in the street since dawn, directing the operations by radio from the police van.

47

"One of the largest manhunts in city history," said the morning news. "Police say they will keep up their exhaustive efforts until they find out exactly what happened to little Alex Selky, age six, missing now from his home in Boston for two days." Then the pictures, the phone number, the appeal for information.

Susan could hear the phones shrilling as she lowered herself like a brittle old woman into a tub full of steaming water. On the edge of the tub lay Alex's blue plastic dolphin that swam around by jerking its tail back and forth when you wound it up. Alex, flushed and wet and slippery in his bath, winding it over and over again. Alex's giggle. Alex learning to wash his own hair, rubbing the lather on his head with his little blunt fingers, his eyes and lips ferociously clamped together to keep out the soap. The smell of Alex's clean soapy skin, his warm breath on her cheek as he kissed her good night.

At eight o'clock Al Menetti came inside with two paper cups of coffee and two gelatinous Danish pastries wrapped in waxed paper. When Susan joined him in the living room, he said, "Share this with me." She obediently sat down and slowly managed to eat a whole sweet roll.

Once again there were dozens of policemen all over the house. One of the officers on the telephones this morning was a woman. "Could I speak to you for a minute, Lieutenant?" she called across the room. Menetti gestured to her to join them.

Officer Hines, a tough, bottom-heavy woman, pulled a chair up to the dining table. "Getting an awful lot of dreams the last two hours," she said.

"Adding up to anything?" Menetti asked.

"Maybe half say they see him near a body of water."

"Great," said Menetti. "How much of the earth is covered with water?"

Officer Hines shrugged. "You ever work with Jennifer Busch?"

"The woman in Providence?"

Officer Hines nodded. "She's not exactly batting four for four, but she hits it now and then."

"Isn't she the one who was consulted in the Patty Hearst case?

She kept saying Patty was in a small dark place? There are a lot of closets in California."

"Yeah, but I worked on one case she was in on, where a guy disappeared one night between work and home. Jennifer Busch kept seeing him *under* water. There was a place along his route home where the highway ran by a river, and, sure enough, we finally found a clump of trees she kept describing, and there was the car, in about eight feet of water, with the guy in it. He'd had a heart attack at the wheel."

Susan looked sharply from one of them to the other.

"She won't work on just any case," continued Officer Hines. "She'll only get involved if she thinks she can actually help. I could give her a call for you." She looked at Susan.

"Do it. Yes, please do it," said Susan.

The woman said heartily, "No problem," and went back to her place at the telephones.

Susan and Menetti sat silently in their chairs for some minutes listening to the phones ring. The officers took names, addresses, phone numbers. They copied down descriptions seen in dreams; they recorded messages from Ouija boards.

"Lieutenant, I think I've got something," one of the telephone men shouted excitedly across the din. "A third sighting of a boy who fits our description, on Newbury Street Thursday morning."

Menetti crossed the floor in two steps. He scanned the facts of the conversation; then he sprinted down the stairs to the communications van, with Susan at his heels. He called for a dozen men to get over to Newbury Street, to go into every store, to get names of every single employee and deliveryman. He gave orders for his men to stay there till noon, stopping everyone, until they found other people who were on Newbury Street at ten on Thursday morning who might also have seen Alex.

"Okay," he said with a smile, turning to Susan. "Now the next thing I want to do is to get in a hypnotist to talk to the people who reported these sightings—and why don't we have you go under hypnosis, too, and the guy on Beacon Street, to see what more you can remember about the street that morning?"

"You know," he said with new energy as they walked back up the stairs, "a case like this is like dominoes. You get nothing, nothing, nothing, and you feel like you're looking at a brick wall, and then suddenly one brick falls, and in a second you've got them all tumbling one after another till the whole case falls into your lap. I can feel it."

THE Newbury Street sightings were a false alarm. Under hypnosis the two people who claimed to have seen Alex gave completely divergent descriptions. One described a child of at least twelve; the other could give no details that were not in the handbill, and in fact had almost surely seen nothing at all. Next Menetti had the man from around the corner put under hypnosis to see if he could remember anything more about the car he saw parked on Beacon Street, or if he could remember seeing Alex approach it. The man identified the car as a light blue Oldsmobile, vintage 1963 or 1964, with rust spots on both doors and one whitewall—on the front-right tire. He insisted he had seen the car parked in exactly the same place at least once earlier in the week, but at no time had he seen Alex approach it. He hadn't seen Alex at all Thursday morning; he'd evidently gone back to shaving before Alex came around the corner.

The police hypnotist came to Susan next. They sat facing each other in two kitchen chairs that Menetti had carried up to Susan's bedroom. "Just relax," said the young doctor. "Focus your eyes right here," and he tapped the bridge of his nose. Susan looked at the spot. In a moment it seemed to glow brightly. They sat in silence. Menetti, behind her on the bed, was perfectly still.

The doctor spoke again. "Now I'm going to count. With each number your eyelids will grow heavier. When I reach ten, your eyes will close."

He began to count, and by the time he reached five, her eyelids dragged downward like lead. At ten, they irresistibly closed.

"Your arms are growing heavy," said the voice. "They are as heavy as lead now." Her arms hung at her sides. "You cannot lift your arms." Susan sat still.

"Try to lift your right arm." She tried. The arm didn't move.

"Good," said the voice. "Now it's the morning of May fifteenth. It's eight forty-five. What are you doing?"

"I'm in the kitchen, putting my students' papers in my folder."

"Where is Alex?"

"He's beside me. He's putting an apple into his lunch bag." Alex brushed his forelock out of his eyes and put the brown lunch bag into his knapsack.

"You ready to go, honey?" asked Susan.

"Yep," he said.

"What about tying that shoelace before you take a trip down the stairs?" Alex giggled. He put down his pack and dropped to his knee to struggle with the lace.

"Honey . . ." said Susan, a little impatient after almost a minute.

"I got it; I can do it," said Alex. He stood up.

The doctor's voice: "All right. You are leaving the kitchen. What do you do?"

"We go downstairs."

"Very good," said the doctor. "Now you are outside. On the front steps." They are. The morning sun, suddenly bright and hot, warms her face and arms. She has to squint a little when she first opens the door and steps outside.

Alex is looking up at her, and the sun makes his hair gleam like polished wood. "Have a good day, sweetheart," she says.

"By, Mommy." She bends down to kiss him, and he puts his right arm around her neck. His left holds his knapsack. His cheek, cool as satin, is against her lips.

"Now, Mrs. Selky," said the doctor, "look down the street to your left. Tell me what you see." She turned her head inside her mind and saw the whole street. As she watched, a truck came around the corner. Two men in running clothes jogged up the street toward her. Then the doctor told her to turn to the right. She described every tree. Every door that opened. The people who passed. It took nearly forty-five minutes to describe it all. She did not see an old blue car; it must have passed her house and turned the corner.

What she could see with staggering immediacy was every lilt of Alex's last steps as she watched him to the corner. The swing of his arms. The turning at the corner to see if she was still watching, the wave of his small right hand. She came out of the trance with a terrible sense of loss, and began to cry.

"It's all right," said Menetti. "The odds are that the car isn't important." Susan didn't bother to explain that that wasn't what she was crying about.

Jennifer Busch, the psychic, arrived in the middle of the afternoon. Her hair was dyed jet black, and she wore a jumper and soft ballet slippers. Her large dark eyes were liquid with sympathy.

"Well, I hope I can help you, dear," she said to Susan. "I'm glad you called; you've been on my mind."

"Do you have an idea . . . do you think you know what's happened to Alex?"

"Don't know yet. I'll tell you one thing, though. When I can see, I know it. When I can't, I say so."

Mrs. Busch asked to be taken to Alex's room. Susan had been careful not to go in there more than once or twice since Alex disappeared. She was saving his room, like a secret cache of something, to be felt with intensity only in deepest private.

Mrs. Busch went straight to the bed and sat down on it, and remained very still a moment or two. "There's been a great deal of loss in this house," she said pointedly to Susan. "A great deal of pain in the little heart that slept here."

"Alex's father and I separated three months ago."

"Um. From the feel of things, I'd say you fought it hard."

"We did," said Susan.

"You feel a great sense of failure."

"Yes."

"Could I have something Alex played with or used when he was happy, please?"

"What? Oh, yes. Sure." Susan looked around, then scooped up Alex's soccer ball from beside his bookcase. Mrs. Busch took it between her plump, short-fingered hands and said, "Good. He played with this with his father?"

"Yes."

Mrs. Busch closed her eyes and sat for some time. Now and then Susan would see a certain flicker or strain cross her face. At last she opened her eyes.

"I can see *him*," she said. "I can't see much else that's any use. He's standing by a window, and the window has cheap venetian blinds, and there's a large road or highway outside, so I'd say it's a motel room."

"You mean, that's what he's doing right this minute?"

"Yes."

"You mean you're sure he's alive, and he's standing by a window? You can tell that wasn't yesterday or . . ."

"Yes," said Mrs. Busch. "I can tell that much."

"Oh, God, he's alive!" said Susan.

"Oh, yes," said Mrs. Busch. "Of course he's alive. I wouldn't have bothered to come if I didn't know that."

ALL afternoon and into the night Susan and Graham were questioned over and over by Al Menetti and a dozen other detectives. Susan had to find names and numbers for virtually every person who ever baby-sat for Alex. They named all the friends they saw regularly, and then the ones not so regularly.

"But why do you want to know about them?" Susan would ask at first. "We haven't seen them for years. Besides, they're perfectly nice." The detectives just kept writing.

One name kept coming up through the afternoon, the father of a child named Bina whom Alex had played with in a day-care center. Bina's mother, Maeve, was a weaver, Susan said. She was very lovely, but once or twice when Alex went to Bina's to play and Susan came to pick him up, she had found that Maeve had "had to go out," and Bina's father, Richard, was there with the children instead. He seemed nice enough, and she never thought more about it, except to wish that Maeve would explain her plans beforehand.

At this point Menetti interrupted. "Susan, you're going to find that a community like this, where people are always coming and going and everyone's allowed to be slightly unconventional, is not always a nice place for people like you." Susan bristled, but Menetti didn't notice. He continued, "For instance, Bina's father, Richard, is a junkie. He's been booked a dozen times for dealing cocaine and heroin, and twice for armed robbery. The last time, he did four years in prison in New Mexico."

Susan felt a cramp of nausea. She had taken pride in her utter tolerance, but she was shocked now—and frightened.

She remembered Richard patiently crawling around on the living-room floor to help Alex find a lost mitten. She remembered prompting Alex to say, "Good-by and thank you." And Richard solemnly coaching Bina to say good-by to Alex and Mrs. Selky.

Susan had passed her teenage years in distress at her step-mother, who greatly simplified her life by dismissing people who were not "our kind." Susan had thought this a very ungenerous and self-limiting way to be. It was chilling to come to understand there are greater kinds of evil than the narrow mind.

It was somewhere around the middle of Saturday afternoon. Graham finally decided to go home to his apartment for an hour to get some clean clothes. When Menetti assigned a detective to go with him, Susan realized that both she and Graham were essentially under house arrest. She hadn't left the house since Thursday evening, and by Saturday she was developing a malaise of physical restlessness like a slight fever. That afternoon she announced that she would go to the supermarket, in spite of a light rain that had begun to fall. She put on her raincoat, and then she went to the pad in the kitchen where she and Alex wrote down items for the shopping list. On the pad was written in Alex's irregular printing, Cheerios, banananas.

Her expression didn't change. Her eyes filled and she stood very still, deep in tears. Alex must have written that Thursday morning. He must have copied the spelling from the Cheerios box—he usually spelled it with one *e*.

She carefully tore off the shopping list and put it in her pocket, and left the house in the company of a policeman. Along every step of the route to the supermarket she saw the streets honey-combed with basements and shafts and alleys and stairwells where a small body could fall or be thrown, hide or be hidden. This was a new horror, a great horror. To see the familiar streets and sidewalks now as sites of danger, scenes of crime.

In the gray of the rainy afternoon the market's yellow fluorescent glow gave the impression of shelter. But the shelves were filled with things that were for Alex, or else not for Alex. The Sugar Pops he could eat at Justine's but not at home, the little snack packs of raisins she never kept enough of in the cupboard. Popcorn—she was out of that—and lemonade now that the hot weather had come. The aisles were also full of people who recognized her. Who felt the same indiscriminate thrill they would feel if she were an actress on a soap opera. And now there she was, in the flesh, the woman who had lost her little boy, the woman they had seen on TV with Vivienne Grant.

Many were discreet, but a surprising number talked loudly to each other about her, or pointed, or stared. A total stranger came up to her and told her she was real sorry about Alex. That they were all praying for him. Then another and another and another spoke to her. Susan thanked them calmly, surprised that her voice was perfectly steady. "Thank you. No, we haven't heard anything. Yes, I feel terrible. Yes, please pray."

A small old woman with an angry face pushed her cart close to Susan's and lit a cigarette. Smoking is illegal in supermarkets, and Susan turned. The woman was staring at her coldly.

"Think you're going to get away with it?" she asked suddenly in a loud voice. "You think you're so smart; you think you can kill your own little boy. How do you feel now, that's what I'd like to know." The woman's eyes were calm, sane, full of hate.

At first Susan barely felt the words land. She just shrugged and moved quickly away, the policeman helping to hurry her cart toward the checkout counter.

But as she walked home the shock began to wear off, and she found her knees and hands shaking. Was that what was going on in people's minds? Those people that you see on the street every day, those people who drop litter on the ground and smoke in the checkout line, with their set resentful faces, is *that* what's going on in their minds? That anger, that twisted loathing? Is that what's all around us?

IN THE weeks that followed Alex's disappearance, Susan had no idea when she slept or how long, or if she was really asleep; and when she did sleep, her dreams were so full of torture that it seemed to drain her more than staying awake.

She had one persistent dream in which she and Alex were walking down a street and they saw Graham coming toward them, hands in pockets and whistling. He had a wonderful swinging walk, and she watched him full of love, waiting for him to notice her and wave. But he did not. Instead he stopped at a strange house and let himself in with his own key. Susan followed him in, and there she found a woman bathing a baby. The baby was Graham's, and the woman was Graham's other wife.

Sometimes Susan woke up heavy with dread and anger, unable to remember what she had dreamed. Whatever it was, the dreams were never as bad as the reality.

She knew she was losing weight, so she refused to weigh herself. But she bathed every day and washed her hair. Her cheeks were often flushed, as May turned to June and the heat rose. Very hard to hide a body in the heat, because of the smell.

The constant noise and the milling of scores of people in and out of the house were a true torture. She often had to fight panic at finding her home completely invaded, finding no room that was hers, no place ever to be alone. To have her house and her heart exposed to the public at this moment, to be robbed of the personal and private in tragedy, was particularly bitter.

For the first two weeks Graham was there every day from eight in the morning until late at night, when he went back to his own apartment to sleep. He'd been good about insisting that his parents stay away. The police had been to West Hartford, Connecticut, to question them, and Susan knew they had found it an ordeal. Alex was their only grandchild, and his disappearance was the most shattering thing to have happened to them in their long lives. If they came, he and Susan would have to spend energy comforting them, and they couldn't afford it.

And Graham was bitter, so angry and guilty. It was terrible for him not to be able to do anything to bring Alex back. He didn't have Susan's numbness. He'd get into fevers of activity, and activity would seem to give rise to hope, and he'd run here and there, call this one and that one, and be suddenly surprised by a great explosion of pain. It was the way he was wired up, the way he'd always been. This day up, that day down, then *boom!* He knew he needed the explosions, but, oh, they hurt when they came. Picking fights, leaving clues to his infidelities, pushing Susan till she fought with him. "That's the last time," she'd finally said. "You need the release, but I don't need the pain. Take it somewhere else. I love you, but you hurt too much."

It was bad enough to be the way he was; was it fair that he should lose so much more because of it?

ONE day at the beginning of the second week, four different people, self-styled psychics, called in to report a similar vision. The first saw Alex in the front seat of a car. The car was moving, and it was a light blue color, and Alex was eating raisins. The second caller also saw Alex in a light blue car, an old-model American sedan. Alex was asleep in the back seat. Policemen were dispatched with pictures of automobiles from 1955 on, to see if the callers could identify the make and year.

Fifteen minutes later a third caller described almost the identical scene. She had had a trance, she said, and she had seen the missing boy lying on the back seat of a blue car. The car was moving, and the driver was a woman, but the caller couldn't see her face in the vision. By that time the first and second callers had each identified the car as an American make from the early 1960s, but even under hypnosis, neither could see the license plate nor describe the driver.

Late that afternoon they had a report from Jennifer Busch. She saw Alex asleep on the back seat of a four-door sedan, a blue or gray car about fifteen years old. The driver was a woman. Mrs. Busch could not see a license plate, but she could see the car pass under a big green sign with white letters: CHARTER OAK BRIDGE. Mrs. Busch had no idea where it was.

But Graham and Susan both knew immediately. "The Charter Oak Bridge is the toll bridge right outside Hartford," Graham said. He wanted to get in a police car and speed up and down the New England Thruway until he found the car himself. He flooded the room with energy and hope.

Menetti contacted highway police in Massachusetts, Connecticut, and New York, and a dragnet was ordered across the three states. On every highway, at every toll plaza from Boston to Bridgeport, police and highway personnel were on the alert for a light blue four-door sedan, American model, year 1963 or 1964, driven by a woman, and carrying a six-year-old boy. Alex's picture was also sent by wire, but it wasn't needed. Every police officer in the East had studied it for the last eight days.

Graham and Susan were sick with hope. They paced up and down the living room and spent much of the evening standing near the bank of telephones, listening to the officers taking the calls. Their eyes met often, speechless and prayerful. They gripped each other's hands. By midnight they were sagging.

In the intervening hours they had learned to think of hope as a vicious tease, the enemy, for in all that time there had been absolutely nothing to confirm what the psychics had seen. There was not a toll collector or highway patrolman who remembered such a car, or boy, or driver. The odds seemed to Graham and Susan too cruel. How on hundreds of miles of highway, in eight hours, could there not be even one woman driving with a six-year-old boy in an old blue car? Susan was more devastated than she had been the night Alex disappeared.

Menetti, who was beginning to look haggard himself, went home about one in the morning, but Graham made no move to follow. Instead he and Susan climbed the stairs together. There were lights still blazing all over the house, with people talking, making coffee, and smoking cigarettes. They lay down together on the bed that had been theirs. Susan sobbed and Graham began to cry openly as well.

After a while Graham whispered, "Susan, let's have another baby."

She held him in the dark, shaking her head vehemently, clenching trembling closed lips. It was so familiar, so bitter, to be hugging his warmth in the dark, her lover, her enemy. She had a piercing headache from crying, and she could feel Graham's tears slip along her collarbone as he cried against her shoulder.

Another baby, because Alex is dead. No, no, no, her head shook in the dark, and she went on crying.

THE next morning Graham was up early. After having a cup of coffee, he went upstairs to Susan's darkened bedroom and looked at her lying prone and still, her face turned away from him. He put a hand on her shoulder in the darkness. "Susan, honey?" he whispered. "Philippe is downstairs. Do you want him to stay?"

"Yes. Tell him I'll be down soon."

Philippe was Jocelyn's "gay cleaning guy," who had been coming to Susan's every other Tuesday for two years. Jocelyn had talked all her friends into trying him. He was easily worth six dollars an hour to Jocelyn, because she dined out on merciless Philippe stories. He cleaned the stove as if it were a fetish. ("When I came home and found him unscrewing the knobs on the stove so he could clean that gunk that gets behind 'em, I asked him to *marry* me," Jocelyn would drawl to an amused audience.) Philippe also read palms and tarot cards and gave his clients a Christmas party every year.

"You're crazy not to use Philippe," Jocelyn had said to Susan, with a look around the kitchen that hinted she thought Susan's housekeeping could stand the improvement. "If I can afford him, *you* can afford him. I'll ask him if he has a free day."

Susan had found Philippe to be everything Jocelyn claimed— sweet, funny, good company, and utterly honest and reliable.

Now she heard a tap on her door. "Suusan," a low voice murmured. "It's Philippe. Do you want me to come iin?" Philippe

59

seemed to stretch and sing all the vowels in his words. He pronounced his own name "Feeleepe," with a long French accent.

"Oh, yes, Philippe. Come in!" Susan sat up on the bed.

"It's so daaark in here," he said, bustling in the door. "Do you mind if I open the curtains?" The sunlight cut painfully across the room in a brilliant ribbon.

"Honey, you are a wreeeck! You look like my dead aunt! Do you know what you should do? You should soak cucumbers in milk and put them on your eyes for fifteen minutes. It just takes the red *right out*. Do you want me to do it for you?"

Susan smiled. Before she could decide what to say, he had bustled purposefully out of the room. Soon he was back with a tray bearing a cup of hot coffee, a glass plate with translucent slices of peeled cucumber, and a bowl of milk. He darted into the bathroom for a towel, which he spread over the pillow.

"Now, lie down flat, and this way the milk won't get on the pillowcase." She closed her eyes and felt something wet plop onto one eyelid, then the other.

He laid a damp washcloth across her eyes and pressed lightly on each eye. "I'll time you. This works *wonders*."

From under her wet bandage she could hear the clink of cup on saucer as Philippe drank his coffee, sitting carefully on the side of the bed. "And he's so good-looking," she could hear Jocelyn saying. "What a waste."

Philippe was short, solid, and muscular, with curly graying hair; he *was* good-looking.

"Now, Susan," he said. "What do you want me to do today? Your house smells like a smoker. Do you want me to do the living room? I don't want to get in the way of the police."

"Would you mind very much just dusting and washing the ashtrays in the living room? Don't bother to vacuum. Then do up here and the kitchen."

"Okay. Do you want me to do anything in Alex's room?"

She stiffened. "Just leave it."

"All right. Time's up." He took off the cloth and scooped up the cucumbers. "There! Much better!"

She smiled and got up to look in the mirror. "Well, Philippe, I don't know what they looked like before, but . . ."

"*And*, you're smiling!"

"Yes, that's true."

"See?" he said proudly. "And your coffee's ready downstairs." He put the things back on his tray and returned to the kitchen.

LATER that morning there was another meeting of the Volunteers to Find Alex Selky. They decided to concentrate this week on getting posters taped inside car windows, so Alex's face would be moving all over the city and the message would go out onto the highways as people began leaving for vacation.

Susan felt the kind of fatigue that leaves you too dragged down to do anything for yourself that might help. All afternoon Menetti questioned her over and over about Graham, Robert, Philippe, everyone. It all seemed to be ground they'd covered before, and she found it boring. Now for the fifteenth time Menetti wanted to know how many people knew she was separated.

"I don't know. A lot."

"What do you mean, did you advertise it?"

"Well, no, but a friend of mine, a psychologist, asked me to be on a TV panel show to talk about how kids adjust to divorce."

Menetti looked as if he needed to spit. "You mean you went on a show where they said, 'This is Professor Susan Selky, she lives in Boston, and her husband has left her'?"

"Well . . ."

"So basically you said to ten thousand people, or fifty thousand, whatever it is, 'I'm a pretty woman, I earn a good salary, I live alone with my young son, and you can find me by looking in the phone book'?"

Susan felt a cold, nauseous twang in the pit of her stomach, followed by a flash of defensive anger. Did Menetti expect a normal person to monitor every decision in terms of the harm that could *conceivably* come of it, one chance in a thousand?

"Why is this so important?" she asked in a much smaller voice, already knowing why, and what he was thinking.

He shook his head. "Never mind. Forget it. Now, can you remember anything else you haven't told me? Any little thing, no matter how small?"

She could not think of anything. It was so sad, so exhausting. She was upset that Menetti was upset.

"DEAR George and Marianne," Susan wrote to Graham's parents. "As I said on the phone, I was glad to get the copy of the sermon you sent me. There has been such a lot of mail—hundreds of letters a day—and a lot of prayers and hopes for Alex. So many people have been kind. If prayers will help, we have them.

"I'm writing because I didn't want to tell you on the phone— the police feel they have a real lead. It is *very* important that the press not get wind of it, because they think they may be able to locate the person quite soon, if nothing alarms him."

The reason she gave for writing was a half-truth. Susan had found to her pain that several things said to friends in her living room had turned up in the Boston papers. The half that was false was the implied hope that her sweet, gallant boy might soon be back in her arms. She just wanted the comfort, however wishful, of saying to someone somewhere that there was good news.

Susan's father used to say you should try to learn something new every day, and that would keep you young. But what she had learned in the last two weeks had changed her to a weary old woman. And then today Menetti had been explaining to her, reluctantly, about a ring of men who produced pornographic photographs and films of little boys. Of course the men didn't kidnap all the boys they used. They didn't have to. Often these men were apparently normal people who made friends with neighborhood kids one way or another—through a Boy Scout troop, a touch-football game. Sometimes the little boys were drugged or forced, but the men were rarely afraid to let them go home afterward. It was not that difficult to convince six- or seven-year-old children that they were profoundly bad and that if they ever told what they had done, they would be punished.

Susan thought of Alex with his Batman cape. All his games and fantasies about power and triumph against evil, the fantasies of a person who feels weak and small. Menetti had said how curious it was that often these sick men did not have to use force on the kids. The man needs the child, and the child realizes that his fantasy has come true—that he's in a position of power, he's got some kind of control over an adult he's never had before.

On the rare occasions that the men were caught, the children were amazingly sly about what had been going on. "He told me my mother and father had moved away and didn't want me any-more, and that I was supposed to live with him now." "He was very nice to me. I called him Dad."

Of course there were the ones who drugged and tortured, and sometimes killed. Less likely to be part of any porn ring. If you catch them at all, you catch them for good. Gacy in Illinois, a man his ex-wife described as kind and gentle. Who turned out to have murdered thirty-three young men and boys and buried them around his house and yard.

Many parents of boys who were ultimately found in Gacy's yard had reported their sons missing and had asked the police for help. But in many states when a child of seven or over disappears, he is presumed a runaway. Two months older, and Alex, too, could have been shrugged off as a runaway.

Menetti had had men combing their records for known child molesters, especially those who specialized in boys. Two days ago they'd come up with a lead pointing to a man called Neil Mooney, twice convicted of sex offenses. Child molesters are the lowest scum in the prison pecking order, and prison officials have trouble protecting them against other inmates. Mooney had been given early parole after being nearly beaten to death in prison. He had been released at the beginning of May.

Mooney had come straight to Boston, and two days after Alex disappeared, he had missed his meeting with his parole officer. That was the lead Susan had written to her parents-in-law about.

Police were working as hard and as fast as they could, trying to trace Mooney's movements without letting the news get around. An ex-con with no money and very few friends would have trouble traveling far, especially if he had a small child with him. He might be underground someplace nearby.

THE end of the second week, at seven in the morning, one of the police called Susan to the phone.

"Susan! This is Una Wright, you know, Una Smith!" (A girl Susan had liked very much in college.) "I'm so happy for you . . . I'm trying not to cry. I had to call you the minute I saw the paper. I went to pick it up a few minutes ago, and when I saw the head-line, I burst into tears on the doorstep."

"Una . . ." Susan did not know what to say. "It's good to hear your voice, but I don't know what you're talking about."

"You don't?" said Una. "The headline in the New York *Herald* this morning says the case is solved."

"It says *what?*" Susan had a wild, irrational moment of hope.

Maybe it was solved and she didn't know it. . . . No. "Una, exactly what does it say? Please read it to me."

"I'll get it." Una sounded chastened and scared. "Here. 'A source close to the family revealed tonight in New York that police are ready to announce a happy ending to the case of little Alex Selky, missing from his home in Boston for fifteen days. Police do not wish to reveal details of the mystery yet, but an announcement is expected later today.'"

Susan felt overcome by a great wave of anxiety. What would this mean? "Thank you for letting me know, Una. It really *was* good to hear from you, and I wish it had been good news."

By the time she dressed and got downstairs, the phones were ringing like banshees, and she could tell from the police response that it was media from all over New England calling to confirm the *Herald*'s story.

Menetti arrived at eight, and Susan knew from his face that he was upset. "It's bad," he said. "It's not going to help at all. We're going to have phones tied up all day undoing the damage, and we're going to lose a lot of momentum." He went to Susan's kitchen phone and put in a call to the New York *Herald.*

They wouldn't, of course, reveal their source. They said they hadn't checked the story with the police because their source was very reliable and they had no reason to doubt him.

Menetti was furious. He told Susan, "I'll have to get the Boston papers to run a story about the *false* story. Otherwise I'll have trouble keeping the department on the case." He was dialing. "And you'll lose your volunteer corps," he said over his shoulder to her. "Yeah! Menetti! Get me the Public Relations office. Look, we've got a big problem here with the Selky case. . . ."

Susan could hear from the next room that the phones were swamped with congratulations. Her heart sank, for, exactly as Menetti had predicted, many calls were from the committee of Volunteers to Find Alex Selky. Those who called could be told, but what about those who did not? What about those who got the story thirdhand, in the bank, at the supermarket? It's all over, he's found; thank God, we can ease our minds. The grateful willingness to be excused, to forget it and return to their own concerns.

When Menetti hung up, he was furious. "This is a mess. I want to know who the reliable source was. Did you tell someone something? Who do you know in New York?"

"I don't know anyone in New York except Robert. We've got a couple of friends there, but none who would hurt us."

"I told you not to tell anyone anything. Didn't I?"

"Yes."

"And did you tell someone? College roomie? Robert?"

"*No!* I wrote a note to my parents-in-law. All I said was things weren't as bad as the papers made them look, but we couldn't afford to have any details get out."

"In other words, you hinted we had a lead."

"I said there was a lead, yes. They're Alex's grandparents! They're worried sick. I didn't see how it could hurt. . . ."

"Didn't it occur to you that the first thing Mrs. Selky would do would be share the good news with Robert?"

"No. It actually didn't."

"Well, think about it! I'd say we got a leak in New York, and we've got Uncle Robert in New York, and I'd check it out."

Susan stared at him. There was so much dislike in his voice when he spoke Robert's name. Why? She actually had opened her mouth to ask him when she stopped herself. A cold new Susan realized for the first time that there was no longer anything she wouldn't believe. In fact she was gradually coming to see the world as the police saw it.

She went to the kitchen and put a call through to Robert.

He greeted her with concern. "Susan! How are you? Is there anything new?"

"There's a story in the morning *Herald* that says that the case is solved. The case is not solved, Robert. I wonder if you can tell me anything about where the paper got that idea?"

"How should I know? Why are you asking me?" He went on the defensive so fast that she knew in her heart that Menetti had guessed right.

"Robert, did your mother tell you we had a lead?"

"I spoke to Mother yesterday."

"Did she tell you we thought there was a lead?"

"Well, she was so encouraged. Why? Did you tell her not to tell me?"

"I hardly told her anything except that I wanted her and Dad to be optimistic, and I didn't want anything about it to turn up in the papers!"

"She didn't say anything about that."

"So what did you do? Did you phone in the story to the *Herald*, or what?"

Robert's voice turned angry. "Wait a minute, Susan. It happens I was at a dinner party last night and I happened to mention that there was going to be a break in the case. One of the gals at the party does book reviews for the *Herald*, which I had forgotten. Besides, it didn't occur to me that she'd tell."

"It didn't occur to you! If you couldn't keep your mouth shut, how did you expect her to, when it's her job?" Susan hung up and started to cry.

The phone rang at once. It was Public Relations for Menetti. At the end of the call he reported to Susan. "They've contacted all the papers and notified the radio and TV stations. None of them will repeat the *Herald* story, but no one will run a story to stop the rumors, either. The news that there's no news doesn't interest them."

When Susan went out late in the afternoon to walk Taxi, she noticed that two of the posters of Alex, with the headline MISS-ING, had been taken down from windows on her block. The glad tidings were spreading.

In the middle of the third week the police took out their bank of phones and left the house. The taxpayer is entitled to that kind of expense for only so long, and Susan had had her allotment for the search effort. In the sudden quiet that fell on the house as the police departed, Susan felt that she was experiencing Alex's death.

Menetti was still with her, and there were, he assured her, a dozen detectives still committed full time to the case. But the house was quiet again, as quiet as it was the afternoon she had sat by the window and waited for Alex to come home. That analogy kept recurring to her, and in midafternoon she went into the living room, placed the chair as it had been that day nineteen days ago, and sat down again to wait.

The phone rang.

It was the afternoon Alex disappeared, and the phone was ringing. If she answered it, her life would wind back, like a movie run backward. Then it would start forward again, but sane this time, the world a sunlit place. On the phone would be the school nurse: "Hello, Mrs. Selky? Alex had a tummy ache, so we thought he should lie down in the office until you could come for him. Yes. Oh, he's fine. Would you like to speak to him?"

"Hello, Mommy?"

Or simply Alex, with his dime, at the deli on the corner. He's stopped to read a comic and lost track of the time. He is kneeling on the seat in the phone booth, so he can dial.

"Hello," he says, quick and stern, "Mommy?"

Or it would be Menetti. "Susan? It's Al. I've finally got some good news for you."

Then the voice on the other end, so sweet and small. "Hello, Mommy?"

The phone is not Menetti.

"Mrs. Selky, this is Mrs. Feldman in the office of the English Department. Dr. Lynn asked me to call you, to tell you how sorry he is. . . ."

"That's kind of him." It was kind of him. It just didn't happen to help. "Tell him I thank him, and—"

"Oh, Mrs. Selky, wait," the secretary cut in, sensing that Susan was going to hang up. "Dr. Lynn, um, wants to know if you're planning to teach your summer courses this year."

"Oh," said Susan. "Tell him that I am not planning to teach."

"I see," said Mrs. Feldman.

"Good," said Susan.

68

"HAVE YOU TALKED TO SUSAN today?" Jocelyn asked Martina, without preamble, when Martina answered the phone. "The police took out the special phone lines this morning. The house must feel like a tomb after what it's been like."

"No, I haven't. I forgot that was today. I've been so busy."

"I don't know, she seems so distant," Jocelyn went on. "She hasn't seemed like herself to me at all for a week or so. Do you think she's all right?"

"What do you mean, all right? How all right can she be?"

"Well, you know, Philippe was here yesterday. He said the police have searched his apartment twice, and they got pretty rough with him the second time."

"He mentioned that," said Martina. "He said they even gave him a lie-detector test."

"Yes, he was in a total panic when he told me. But you know what he did? He said he took one look at Susan when he was over there for his day and decided she was such a wreck, he never even mentioned the test to her. He said he didn't want to upset her any more. So he spent the whole afternoon in the kitchen scrubbing the oven. Isn't that sweet?"

Martina agreed. She said she was sorry she couldn't get to see Susan before the weekend. She would speak to Jocelyn soon.

IT WAS midmorning, four weeks to the day since Alex disappeared. The mail continued to pour in for Susan and Graham, and the phone rang often. Menetti was still constantly in and out of the house, and there were still a dozen detectives working on the case, but Susan saw far less of them.

She was opening the mail, sorting it into piles of notes from personal friends, well-wishes from strangers, visions from the Lord, and lunatic abuse. She was surprised that she heard so much less from people she knew than she did from strangers.

She didn't know yet how to field the attacks. She dropped the notes into the wastebasket without reading more than a line, the way one hangs up on an obscene phone caller after the first few words. But they yammered at her with their malicious voices when she was too tired to knock them away. You killed him your-self. Your husband killed him. You killed him together and you're pretending to be separated so the police won't think you're con-spiring. You're guilty because you did it. You're guilty because you were negligent; you endangered your own child's life to save yourself walking a block. You're an unfit mother who deserved to lose your child. Have you learned your lesson? God has done this to show you. And I'm so happy you got what you deserved.

In the late nights, alone, she sometimes crossed the line and believed that she was guilty, that she had risked his life to save herself walking a block, that she did deserve to lose Alex.

Menetti buzzed her from downstairs, and she let him in. "All alone?" was his first question. Yes, she was, today. Graham came over only when there was a really promising lead. Margaret Mayo was at work, and Susan's friends were very busy.

"I'm having this root canal done, but I'm thinking of you. . . ."

"As soon as I get the boys off to summer camp I'll be free again. I'll try to drop by on Sunday."

She could understand. Their lives did have to go on. She only wished hers could. They *had* given tremendously of their time.

"Yes," she said to Menetti, "I'm holding the fort. Has anything happened?"

"Well, we found Neil Mooney."

"And?" Susan's heart was cold with fear.

"And it's a dead end. His parole officer called me last night at home to say Mooney had walked into his office at five in the afternoon. He's been in Belmont all this time and had no idea we were looking for him. He told us exactly what he's been doing since his release from prison, and we checked everything out. His story stands up."

"Oh," said Susan. What was she supposed to say? No news was good news. No news was bad news. All news was bad news.

THE Volunteers to Find Alex Selky called a meeting at Susan's house for the following Wednesday. Susan phoned several televi-sion stations to see if they'd like to cover the meeting. It was essential that people remember Alex and that they see his face, that people keep looking for him. Are there new leads? the producers wanted to know. There were not. Oh, said the producers, then we'll pass.

The meeting of the volunteers attracted a smaller group than in the beginning. Jocelyn and Martina were there, of course, and perhaps two dozen others, including Graham, Margaret Mayo, TJ, and Annie. It was an awkward hour. People entered in twos and threes, no longer in the stunned, frightened silence that had filled them all at the first news, but now chatting with each other about work, play, vacations, camp, and kids. Susan could hear their voices on the stairs; then she'd hear them suddenly hush themselves as they reached the landing, as if they'd caught themselves telling jokes at a funeral.

At the meeting it was agreed that the main objective now was to keep people interested. Graham said, "I saw a guy on the street the other day look at a poster as he passed and say to his companion, 'Whatever happened about that kid? They must have found him by now.'

"What we have to do," Graham continued, "is demonstrate that the search is active. If people only see that same first handbill, they will stop seeing it, or stop believing it."

Muriel Kopp spoke from the depths of the blue sofa. "Graham, if you'd like to go to a four-color poster, my office will donate the graphics. I can have my printer do the job at cost."

"Muriel, thank you." Graham turned to Susan, who was sitting in a chair behind him. "Should we?" he whispered.

"Absolutely," she agreed.

"And until we can get new posters ready, Susan has an interim plan." Graham held up a brown paper bag. "We had a dozen rubber stamps made up that say STILL." He reached into the bag and held up a stamp with a wooden handle. "And we've got a dozen red ink pads. If each of you would volunteer to be responsible for an area of the city, we could get around and stamp the handbills in red with the word STILL above MISSING."

"I'll do out around the Fen," said Jocelyn.

"I'll take Beacon Hill," spoke up a painter whose son and Alex were good friends.

"That's great. Thank you," said Graham.

Martina and her husband offered to do the South End, and Muriel Kopp volunteered for the Harvard Square area. Section by section the others accounted for the whole map. They agreed that if nothing happened in the next two weeks, they would meet again to deploy the new color poster.

It was stifling hot out in Saugus that third week in June. Al Menetti had been late getting home from work again tonight and had had to eat a plate of stiff food Pat had kept for him in the oven. In this heat she wasn't going to cook dinner twice.

"Look at you," she said when he laid down his fork. "Your clothes are hanging on you. You must have lost ten pounds!"

"Good," he said. "I needed to." That was true, but still his cheeks were sunken. Losing weight had left him drawn-looking.

Now he was upstairs in the bedroom going over reports on the Selky case. There were more than seven hundred of them—phone conversations, interviews, polygraph tests, and so on. He'd spent so many hours reading them, he should have had them memorized. Pat said as much. "I have," he said, pressing his lips together. He went over and over them anyway.

As soon as Pat had the three youngest kids tucked in their beds, she invited Al to come out onto the patio with her for some coffee and cake.

The night was warm, moist, and starry. Pat handed him a cup of instant Sanka and a plate of pound cake with toasted coconut. He really didn't want it, but he knew that if there was one thing his placid wife disliked, it was feeling fat by herself.

"So," he said after a long drink of the night's sweet quiet. He hadn't taken an hour to relax with Pat for a good long time. "How've you been?"

"Oh, pretty good, thanks. Want to hear about Eugene wetting his bed?"

"He's wetting his bed again? Is something wrong with him?"

"Who knows? The doctor said just to be very patient and wait for him to grow out of it."

"Yeah, well, let's hope so, because that kind of thing can embarrass a guy at college."

Al drank his coffee and looked at the stars, and in seconds was back on Fremont Street. He could see that morning as if he had been there. He could see that little boy wave to his mother and turn the corner. He could see him walk down the street, giving a little skip now and then, the way Eugene did.

"So, Al," said Pat, "did it hurt you much when the rumor went around that the Selky case had been solved?"

"Yeah, it did. I don't think Susan realized how much it hurt. But the last day or two, the more I go over those reports, the more I have a creeping suspicion I've been on the wrong track since the beginning."

"Really? Have you come up with something?"

"As I told you, I made a dumb move the first day, looking for a custody fight. I didn't call for bloodhounds right away. . . ."

"But you did what would have been right ninety percent of the time."

He waved her remark away. "It was a mistake. So I went the other way after that. I said, 'Okay, it's a stranger. It's no one these people know. It's a psycho killer, it's a child molester, it's a poor deranged woman who wants a kid.' I've even found myself very seriously listening to these psychics. It's interesting. Just about all of them believe the boy is alive."

"But last week you were dragging the South Bay for him."

"Yeah, we were. Thank God Susan never heard about that. We dragged for two days. Of course he wasn't there."

"So do you have a new theory?"

"Susan is convinced that the boy is alive somewhere and that the media are her hope. She feels that if she keeps the faith and keeps looking for Alex and waiting for him to come home, sooner or later someone will recognize him, and it will happen."

"Does she really believe that?"

Al said, "I don't know. She's one very determined lady. It's like

73

asking the Pope if he believes in God. Anyway, I've been going right down the line with her. I've checked records, I've combed the books, I've checked into every possible thing you can trace about perverts and child molesters and pornography rings and kidnappers. Lately I've begun to suspect I've led myself down the garden path."

"Oh, yes?" Pat had just realized that another very small slice of cake wasn't going to kill her.

"I don't know that I'm looking for a stranger, and I don't know that I'm looking for a live boy. Most murders are committed by people who know the victim. This was a bright kid, and his mother had talked to him about going with strangers. That's the warning bell I kept ignoring. Why would he go with someone he didn't know? If he was forced, how come nobody saw him struggle or heard him scream? The street was full of people."

"Are you saying you think it was done by someone he knew?"

Al shrugged. "It's possible. I *want* to believe what the mother believes, but the other thing is very, very possible. I can't do my job right if I don't check it out."

"Do you suspect someone in particular?" asked Pat.

Menetti didn't answer. He looked at his fingernails. She knew she wouldn't hear any more tonight.

ON THE Monday of the first week of July the producer of "A.M. Boston" called Susan. He said, "Mrs. Selky, we've just received word that another child, a little five-year-old girl, has disappeared in South Boston. The little girl's mother has agreed to appear on our show tomorrow morning, and we'll have a psychologist with us to talk about what happens to a family when a child disappears. I wondered if you'd be willing to join us."

"If you will show Alex's picture on the air," Susan replied. "And if you'll make it very clear that the case is active and we want the viewers to keep looking for him."

"Fine," he said. "Makeup call is at six thirty, and we're on the air live from eight to nine. We won't know until tomorrow which segment you'll be on, so plan to be with us for the whole show."

SUSAN and the other mother sat side by side in the makeup room. The makeup artists were husband and wife, their identical black kits set up on a counter. Susan watched in the mirror as the woman worked on her, nodding when Susan said she would like as little as possible, please. On went the mascara and scarlet lipstick anyway. This was a soft-news show, or more truthfully, an entertainment show, and the viewers were not entertained by guests who looked chronically ill under the lights.

The makeup man was chattering to the missing girl's mother, a light-skinned black woman named Jannette. Her round face was yellow with worry, but she was excited about being on a TV show. "Do you usually wear eye shadow, darling?" babbled the makeup man. "Now we are going to give you highlighter on the cheekbones, here and here."

Susan felt like shouting, Hey, buster, this woman has just lost a child! But Jannette seemed distracted in spite of herself. "Here?" she asked, pointing to her cheek.

"*No, here,*" said the makeup man. "Then you put the cheek color here." He brushed on powdered rouge of a purple tone to create the impression of hollows. "And *voilà!* Cheekbones!"

Jannette looked at herself intently. She seemed reluctant to yield her chair to the Chinese actor who was going to demonstrate his recipe for omelets on the segment after theirs.

The producer's assistant showed them to the greenroom, where they were to wait. "Of course it isn't really green," said the assistant. "That's just a show-business term." Susan already knew that, but Jannette did not, and she seemed quite interested. "I heard them say that on Johnny Carson," she remarked.

Five minutes before the show was to begin, two policemen were shown into the greenroom. "Mrs. Smith?" one asked. Jannette identified herself. Susan realized later that she was surprised that they didn't even ask to see her privately. "We've found your

75

little girl, Mrs. Smith," said the officer. "She's dead. The hatch was partly open on your neighbor's cistern. She fell in and drowned." Jannette simply looked up at them with a puzzled expression until she was led away, and Susan was left to stare at the Chinese actor in stunned silence.

A few minutes before her segment the producer's assistant came in and bent over Susan. She talked to her as a nurse speaks to a sick child. "You going to be all right, dear? Would you like a glass of water? . . . Okay, what we're going to do is send you on with the psychologist by yourself. Do you feel up to it? . . . Good girl!" Susan wanted very badly to slap her face.

In the studio, Susan and the psychologist were introduced. Dr. Mandelbaum was a painfully thin young man with friendly eyes. They stood in the relative darkness behind the lights and cameras, watching the show's host finish a segment with a state senator. When it was over, the assistant rushed Susan and the psychologist into the blue-white bath of light on the set. "We have sixty seconds to get you both miked and settled," she said.

A sound man was clipping a tiny microphone onto Susan's blouse. The assistant was burbling, "We've given you eleven minutes, because we thought there were going to be three of you. Eleven minutes can be a long time under these hot lights, but don't be nervous. Valerie Scott will be interviewing you. Oh, here's our Valerie. Valerie, this is Mrs. Selky, and this is Dr. Mandelbaum. Okay, ready?" The assistant favored them with her widest smile and skipped off the set.

They sat in low armchairs around a plastic-topped coffee table, and the segment began. Valerie Scott explained that Mrs. Smith, whose presence on the show had been announced, was not with them because her little girl had, tragically, been found. She re-told the story of Alex's disappearance more than six weeks before, and while she talked, Susan saw in the monitor that they were broadcasting Alex's picture. For a moment she got lost in that laughing face. There was Alex, in a freeze-action frame. In a moment he would start moving, finish his laugh.

"Mrs. Selky, you were in the greenroom with Mrs. Smith just

a few minutes ago when police came to tell her that her little girl had been found, dead. Can you tell us what your feelings were at that moment?"

"Why, yes," said Susan. "I thought, When you have a baby, you look forward to protecting him and guiding him in gentle stages through all the hard things about growing up. And now suddenly her little girl has gone on ahead of her into the experience that we all fear the most."

Valerie Scott seemed to expect more. "It must have been a very *sad* moment," she prompted.

Susan looked as if she were not sure what the word meant. "Well . . . yes," she agreed. Valerie turned to Dr. Mandelbaum, who delivered what was expected of him. Death of a child, deeply disorienting, psychologists feel, deepest grief known. It flowed over Susan like a stream flowing over a rock.

"Mrs. Selky's position is different from Mrs. Smith's," Valerie resumed, "in that her little boy has disappeared and she has no way of knowing if he's dead or not. Tell me, Mrs. Selky, are there any new leads?"

Obediently Susan described the situation. No new leads, but every reason to hope that someone had Alex and was taking good care of him. Essential for viewers to memorize his face, to watch for him, and report anything they saw.

"Your confidence is inspiring, but there must be times when you fear that knock on the door, bringing you the same news that Mrs. Smith heard this morning?" Susan looked at the sleek, polished face that asked her the question. Tell us you're afraid, Mrs. Selky. Break down and cry. Give it to us, Mrs. Selky.

Susan wondered if Menetti were watching. She said, "Yes, of course, but fears are different from faith. I have faith that my son is alive. I believe that if he were gone from the earth, I would know it. Faith is a power in itself, and it happens to be the only one I have left. If we care about missing children like Alex, if we all remember them and look for them, then there is hope that they will be recognized and returned. If we don't, then, alive or not, there's no hope."

77

"Are you saying that if you give up hope, the police will stop searching for Alex?"

"Not only the police. Your viewers. Everyone. If Alex is alive, sooner or later someone may see him. If I keep faith that he's alive, if I keep asking for help to look for him, there's a chance that he will be brought home. If I don't, there isn't. Therefore, I believe he is alive."

"Isn't that a non sequitur, Mrs. Selky?"

"No."

Dr. Mandelbaum spoke up, to Valerie's obvious relief. "Mrs. Selky is in a very unusual situation from a psychologist's point of view, because in a normal mourning situation, there comes a point when the mourner must pick up the pieces of his life and go on. But in the case of an unknown fate, the person is prevented from going on to the healing stage of grief. The mourner is frozen in the most painful moment of human experience. We saw this phenomenon during the Vietnam War, with the families of soldiers missing in action."

Susan listened gratefully as Dr. Mandelbaum droned on until the end of the segment. Valerie broke in when she got a thirty-second sign from a technician, and cued the picture of Alex again, and that was all Susan wanted.

IN THE next few days Susan began to receive phone calls from all over the country from other parents who had lost children. Their stories were heartbreaking, and Susan began to feel that she had a responsibility to help all of these parents alone in their nightmares, if her situation could help anybody else. It was one of the thoughts that kept her facing the media over and over again in the weeks to come. Every time she thought of stopping, she would hear one more story of parents who had almost given up when some local newspaper ran one last squib and their child was recognized and brought home.

Susan fell into the habit of beginning her days by sitting at the window from eight to nine, drinking a cup of tea and watching the sidewalk below. She gazed down at the steaming hot neighborhood street, nearly immobile except for her watchful eyes. By eight thirty almost every morning she would see Menetti's car pull up. He would get out and start from her doorstep to walk down the street exactly as Alex had. When he got to the corner, he stopped and looked back up the street, as Alex had. Then he turned the corner and disappeared, as Alex had.

Any morning Menetti didn't come, Susan got depressed.

In mid-July Susan relented and agreed to let her father and stepmother come east from Ohio for the weekend. They would be careful not to be any bother. They would stay at a hotel. Susan dreaded the visit. For years the safest and happiest topic of conversation they shared had been Alex.

They made it very easy for her. Her father was a tall, thin, quiet man in his mid-seventies. At home he kept to himself and played a lot of golf. Susan's stepmother, Connie, looked twenty years younger than her husband, having been plucked and dyed and face-lifted within an inch of her life. She was not a silly woman, but silence made her anxious and this led her often to chatter when she had nothing to say.

The first night for a special extravagance they took Susan to dinner at Locke-Ober's. She was touched to note that her father as well as Connie worked hard at maintaining a flow of conversation. They talked about the flavor of everything; neither remarked that Susan was eating none of her lobster soufflé.

The next evening they took her to see the road company of *Annie*. "We're so lucky it's here. It's the one play your father really wanted to see," Connie confided. There was no way they could have known that Alex had asked for the sound track of *Annie* for Christmas and played it noon and night till he could sing every song. (Alex in the tub, draped with suds from his bubble bath, belting, *"Lucky me! Lucky me! Look at what I'm dripping with . . . little girls."*)

After the theater Susan's father said, "Why don't you come back to the hotel for a nightcap, since we won't see you in the morning?" She wanted so much to go home and be alone, but she made herself say she'd love to.

Her father had a brandy, which Connie and Susan declined. Susan sat uncomfortably in a chair while they sat on their beds.

"Susan," said her father, looking down at his fingernails. "I'm very proud of the way you're handling this." Susan froze in her chair. If he said any more, she would cry. But he didn't.

"Well," he said, standing up. "It was lovely to see you, honey. Thank you for—"

"Thank you for a lovely time, Daddy."

"And here's a little something . . . Just in case . . ." He took from the dresser a large gaily wrapped package and handed it to her. The card said, *To my grandson on his birthday.*

LATE on a Monday afternoon, about a week after her father's visit, Susan's phone rang. It was Menetti. He hadn't been near the neighborhood all day, and she'd been feeling very low.

"Susan. I just wanted to see if you were home."

"I'm home. You didn't come by this morning."

"I'm afraid I was waiting on some news. I'm still expecting a call any minute, but in case it doesn't come in soon, I wanted to know where to reach you this evening."

"What's happened?" She knew from his voice it wasn't good.

"Well, I got a call from Philadelphia PD today. Some kids early this morning found a plastic bag with a body in the woods down there."

She felt a deep wallop of pain, as if everything inside her had just cracked up the middle.

"You think it's Alex."

"Susan, it's a small body. They didn't know when they called me if it was male or female. We're waiting for the coroner's report. It's taking a while."

"Okay," she said. "I'll be here."

She sat a moment by herself in the afternoon light and then called Graham. He wasn't home. She told Naomi, and Naomi said she'd find him right away. Graham arrived in less than an hour. "Did he call back yet?" was all he said as he burst in the door. She shook her head.

"Is it evil for me to pray it's not Alex?" she asked. Graham shook his head, and they sat down together on the couch.

"We always knew it might be this," he said.

"I know," she whispered.

The call came at eight o'clock. By that time dusk had fallen in the room, but they hadn't turned on the lights. Graham leaped to answer it.

"It's a female," said Menetti. "The body was incomplete; that's why it took so long. They make her four or five inches taller than Alex, probably nine years old." As he listened, Graham's face telegraphed the news to Susan, an expression of awesome relief.

"The details don't correlate with any kid who's been reported missing," Menetti was saying.

"You mean a nine-year-old girl could disappear and no one would report it?"

"Yeah. Hey, Graham, tell Susan good night for me. Tell her I'm glad."

"I will, Al. Thank you."

Graham went back and took Susan in his arms. "What are these, tears?" he said, holding her.

"I'm so relieved. . . ." Her voice was trembling. "It's disgusting, but I thank God. I feel like celebrating."

"Me, too! Let's go eat something spicy and drink champagne."

"Let's call TJ and Annie!"

"No, let's just be together."

"Okay. Let's go!"

But halfway through dinner the mood was spoiled. Susan couldn't eat. She felt choked at the thought of happiness, as if that alone was a betrayal of Alex.

"Susan," said Graham, "you know it could have been Alex."

"I know that. Don't you think I know that?"

"I think you know it in your head, but I don't see you doing anything to prepare yourself for it."

"What do you mean?"

"Honey, if that call tonight had gone the other way, or if we just don't ever hear anything again . . ."

"Yes?" she said coldly.

"What I'm trying to say is, there may come a time when you will have to consider accepting . . ."

"Accepting what? That it's too painful to go on hoping, so I should give up on him? That I should cut him off to save myself the inconvenience of missing him?"

"Not of missing him, Susan. We'll miss him for the rest of our lives. Of trying to save him if he can't be saved. Susan, for your own good . . ."

"For *my* own good! What about *our* own good? Am I in this by myself now? Isn't he your son, too?"

Graham looked down at the table and sighed. Her eyes gleamed with an anger he dreaded because it seemed to come from somebody else who now and then woke up inside her.

"Of course he's my son, too," he said. "I just wanted to talk about you because you worry me."

"So I'm in trouble over this, but you're perfectly fine, eh? Crazy Susan, can't cope? Well, I'm coping, Graham. And don't tell me I haven't had plenty to cope with."

"Please, Susan. I didn't mean anything like that, and in your heart you know I didn't. Of course I'm having trouble; I'm having more trouble than I ever thought I could bear."

She glared at him. "Well, maybe you're bearing up so well because you didn't care so much in the first place. You didn't care enough to resist breaking up his home, did you?"

Graham's face fell and he looked awful, but his voice was still soft as he said, "Susan, when you get like this, you say things that are very hard to forgive."

She knew it was true. She knew it was precisely her ruthless rage when she was hurt that had contributed to the crash of the marriage. "I want to go home," she said. And the two people inside her, the sane one and the hurt one, fought all the way home, trying to say to Graham that she knew how wrong she was. But her eyes and throat were still dry with anger—at what, she wasn't even sure—when they parted in silence. It wasn't until the door closed behind him that she started to cry.

She didn't hear from Graham for almost a week. In fact she didn't hear from anybody not connected with the case. *Boston* magazine sent a reporter to do a story with her. Susan found it a relief to talk to someone who listened with intelligence, who wouldn't then go away in pain and never call again.

Susan knew now that some people she'd known for years were crossing the street when they saw her, so they wouldn't have to chat. She didn't blame them, but she could have used the contact, a daily smile and a "Hello, how are you?"

But, then, what could she answer?

She felt sure that Graham would at least come back on Alex's birthday. He wouldn't let her spend that day alone.

The phones were especially busy all that muggy rainy day of Alex Selky's seventh birthday. The Boston papers ran his picture and a recap of his disappearance for the occasion, and Susan appeared on a talk show called "Live at Noon." Sometimes now, when she spoke to strangers about Alex, she was dry and matter-of-fact, even to the point of being slightly ironic, as people are when they are deeply immersed in a topic and explaining it for the hundredth time to novices. Her control surprised her, since sometimes she seemed to weep all day. After her segment she heard two of the light-crew men talking in the hall.

"I've been covering news for twenty years," one said, "but that's one of the toughest cookies I've ever seen."

"Yeah, very tough lady. . . ." They went on down the hall.

Compared to what? thought Susan. How many mothers have you known whose sons have been missing for seventy-three days?

Martina called in the middle of that afternoon.

"Hi, Susan," she said in a worried voice. "How are you?"

"I've had better days, actually. This is Alex's birthday."

"Oh, I know," said Martina. She seemed embarrassed.

"Thank you," Susan said softly. "I'm glad you remembered."

After a while Susan tried to call Jocelyn. She thought she would like to have Jocelyn and Justine come for tea. She'd go out and get some little cakes. She would like to do something happy for Alex today. . . . There was no answer at Jocelyn's.

It wasn't until nearly suppertime that it occurred to her that Graham might not come. He couldn't really be meaning to stay away today. By nightfall, when he had still not phoned, she was paralyzed with leaden depression.

At nine o'clock she heard steps on the stairs. Graham? No, not his step.

TJ called, "Susan? Susan? Are you here?" Then he let himself in and walked into the living room. He turned on a lamp and went over to where she sat by the window, scooped her up, and sat down, cradling her against his chest.

"Happy birthday," he whispered, and she nodded against his chest and began to cry, and went on for a long time.

When she felt emptied of tears at last, Susan got up and made some tea. They sat together by the fireplace, and she asked TJ politely, "Where's Annie?"

"She had a concert tonight. She sent you her love and said to tell you she's going to sing the lullaby for Alex." Susan nodded. Annie was a cellist, and Alex loved to listen to her play and sing. Last year on his birthday, TJ and Annie had come at bedtime as a surprise and serenaded Alex under his window.

> *"Hushaby ... Don't you cry*
> *Go to sleep, Little Baby.*
> *When you wake, you will find*
> *All the pretty little horses."*

"Where's Graham?" TJ asked softly.

Susan shrugged and shook her head. TJ didn't press it.

"Today," said TJ, "I thought about the day Alex was born. I got to see him through the nursery window in the evening. He had a little straight nose that looked just like Graham's. Graham and I could see one of his little fists outside the blanket. You were asleep, but I sneaked in and left you flowers, remember? You looked like you were having the sweetest dream."

"I was." There had been no Alex, and then all in one day he was in their lives. And now there was no Alex again. Who could have dreamed the time between that day and this one would be so short?

"Remember the day he was christened? He yelled when the minister put the water on his head. He looked furious to wake up like that, and we all had trouble not to laugh. I was afraid I'd drop him when you handed him to me."

TJ reached into his pocket and took out a jeweler's box, which he handed to Susan. She opened it, and in it found a small Swiss wristwatch on a child's band; it was engraved on the back. To AGS FROM TJF, JULY 27, 1980.

"I had it done in the spring," whispered TJ.

Susan realized it was the first time in all the years she had known him she'd seen TJ crying. "He gave us so much joy," she said. "We didn't know we weren't going to have time to give him all the things he deserved."

Out of words, joined in one warmth but in their heads each alone with his grief, they sat in silence for a long half hour.

Then through the living-room window they saw a bright light from a car driving slowly down the street. TJ went to the window and leaned out. The light careened around the walls.

"Police car," he said. The light went out and the motor sound died. Susan froze as she heard him say, "They've got Graham. They're holding him up." TJ and Susan looked at each other in bewilderment. Then TJ leaped down the stairs.

It seemed to Susan to take forever for them to get Graham up one step at a time. She could hear one of the policemen saying, "Easy. Easy. *Don't rush.*"

Then TJ said, "You're okay." And a voice that might have been Graham's, if he had rags in his mouth, said something. When she saw him come through the door, she knew it was a measure of how much she had changed that she didn't make a sound.

Graham's face was battered, as if it had been stamped on. One eye was swollen shut. It was a mottled purplish blue. His lips, too, were swollen and bloody from where they'd been sliced through by his own teeth. He held one arm stiffly at his side, but when she looked at it fearfully, he said, trying not to move his lips, "'S bruised. Not broken."

TJ helped him to a chair as one of the policemen said, "He wouldn't let us take him to a hospital, missus. He said he had to get here. He oughta have that arm x-rayed."

"He oughta have everything x-rayed," said the other one.

"I'll go tomorrow," Graham enunciated with great care.

"What happened? Where did you find him?" asked Susan.

"North Cambridge. From what we gather, he got what he thought was a ransom call. And instead of calling the police, he decided to walk into an alley by himself at ten o'clock at night carrying ten thousand dollars in cash."

Susan's heart nearly stopped. "Good God!" said TJ. They both stared at Graham.

"I . . . got this call from some woman," Graham said. It hurt him to breathe, so the words came out of his swollen lips in brief gasps. "She said she had . . . Alex. She said he . . . got sick. So she was scared. She didn't dare call . . . a doctor for him. She said she'd sell him back . . . to me . . . for ten thousand dollars."

"Didn't you ask to speak to him?" Susan asked in a tiny voice.

Graham nodded. "I heard . . . this little voice say, 'Hi, Daddy.' " Here Susan saw his one open eye fill with tears. "I told her . . . it wasn't enough. . . . I couldn't tell if it was Alex. She said he had a fever and . . . and had . . . to go back to bed."

"But why didn't you call the police?" asked TJ.

"She said . . . if I did . . . she'd leave him alone and he might die. She said she had a boy friend on . . . the police, and she would know if . . . I called . . . them."

"But where did you get the money?" asked Susan. It was more than she and Graham had ever had at one time, except for the down payment on the house.

"Borrowed it . . . two thousand from Dad . . . eight thousand from Robert."

"We gotta be getting back," said the first policeman.

Susan nodded. "Thank you for bringing him home."

"I'd rather have taken him to a hospital," said the second policeman. "You be sure he goes first thing in the morning."

The first policeman looked at Susan and said, "I wish he'd of called us first, Mrs. Selky." She nodded as if to say, I know, and then he asked, "Do you want us to help get him into bed?"

"Yes, thank you."

The two gently hoisted Graham to his feet, and he put his good arm around one pair of blue shoulders. Susan went up the stairs before them, turning on the lights, while the two officers half pushed, half lifted Graham up to the bedroom. Then they said their good-nights.

"I'll go out with them and lock up," said TJ, who had followed them. He put his arms gently around Graham and held him briefly. "You dumb jerk," he whispered. Graham tapped TJ's shoulder with his palm and nodded.

When they were alone, Susan helped Graham undress and painstakingly inched his body into bed. "Light out?" she whispered. He nodded. In the darkness she felt him reach his hand toward her. She knelt beside the bed. With his good arm he drew her against him and held her hard; through the tears and the swollen mouth she could hardly hear what he whispered.

"I wanted . . . so much . . . to bring him home to you."

Later she slipped into bed beside him in the dark, trying not to make the mattress bobble, and spent the night, half awake, half sitting, with his mauled face supported against her shoulder. The breath in his mangled nose made a thin rasping sound, as if wheezing and fluttering through something torn deep inside him.

GRAHAM had cracked ribs and multiple bruises. The doctors strapped the ribs in place, and gave him a wide cloth belt with many buckles for support. The first evening when Susan went to see him in the hospital, he seemed very low. He looked over at the door when she came in, as if he'd been waiting for her, and held out his hand. She stood by his bed holding it until it was time to go. The second evening his color was better and he was breathing more easily. "I can leave tomorrow," he told her.

"I know. I just saw the doctor. You'll have to be still, though."

Graham nodded. "I'd like to come home," he said.

She looked at him as if she were seeing something behind his eyes. "Okay," she said. He gave her his hand again, and again she stood quietly, holding it.

"Do you want me to come back for you?" she asked.

He shook his head. "TJ will bring me. He'll go get my stuff from Naomi."

"Okay. I'll see you tomorrow, then."

"Okay." He pressed her hand before he let it go.

On the way to the elevator she met Naomi. Neither smiled as they approached each other. Susan said, "Hello," and Naomi nodded. They were poised face to face for a moment, each holding an orange visitor's card. Then they passed each other.

Al Menetti had been to see Graham in the hospital twice, and now he came in every day to hear the story over and over, hoping for something that would tell him where to start looking. But it was useless. The ransom call could have come from anywhere, and the two men who beat Graham had worn ski masks. Graham couldn't even say how tall they were. Menetti kept asking why Graham hadn't called him the minute he got the ransom demand. No matter how often he heard the explanation, it didn't seem to satisfy him.

Philippe was delighted to find Graham home again when he came to clean. He sat on the edge of the bed and demanded to hear all about each injury. Then he told Graham in generous detail about the time he had broken his leg in two places while skiing. When he'd finished his cleaning, he laid a tea tray for himself, Graham, and Susan and carried it up to Graham's room.

He took a sip of his tea. "Susan, did Jocelyn tell you I have a new client? He's a channel."

"A channel?" asked Susan and Graham together.

"Like a medium. You know, a channel from the other side. He showed me a videotape of one of his sessions."

"What was it like?"

"Oh, it was weird. He rolled his eyes, then he began to talk in this odd sort of chipmunk voice." Philippe began reciting nonsense syllables in a high, electronic-type whine.

"Don't make me laugh, Philippe," said Graham with his hand against his sore ribs.

"Oh, sorry. Shall I go on?"

"Yes, please. Just don't be funny."

"Well, it works like this. He's a channel for this spirit called Yasha, and he said I could come to a session and ask Yasha a question. I'm going Friday to ask him about Alex."

"Thank you, Philippe."

"You're welcome. I doubt if he can tell me any more than the cards, but there's no point not trying."

Graham was watching Susan. He saw in her face that beginning query: Could this be it? Could this help? Wanting to distract

her, he said, "Do the cards for me, Philippe. Find out how long it will be before I can turn over in bed without yelling."

"You can't just ask the cards a question like that," said Philippe seriously. "They'll only answer what they want to, you know."

"That's okay, Philippe. I'll take my chances." Philippe went to get a deck of cards from the living room. Graham smiled at Susan. "See," he said softly, "a few swift kicks in the head, and even I believe in fortune-tellers."

Philippe returned and smoothed the bed sheet beside Graham to make a place for cards. "I'll shuffle them," he said to Graham, "and you cut. Good. Okay, now watch. I lay them out in this pattern." He set out the cards as they came from the top of the deck. "And then I interpret the way they lie in relation to one another. For instance, this one can mean house, or home, and now . . . oh, the black man . . . that could be the devil or the hangman or a dark, handsome stranger, depending . . ." He let the sentence hang, then he sat looking at the cards with a puzzled expression that gradually deepened to a look of distress.

"Okay, Philippe," said Graham. "Let's have it. There's the house and the black man, and there's the queen of hearts right beside it, which is Susan, of course. The devil is going to break into the house and steal the silverware, and then Susan is going to run away with him."

"Well, you may think it's funny," said Philippe, "but if that card is the hangman, then someone in this house is going to be arrested." He scooped up his cards and left the room.

AUGUST in Boston is always a punishment of stifling gritty heat, white and glaring in the daytime, scarlet and noisy at night. Along the riverbank that summer the Esplanade was filled late into the evening with half-naked bodies in shorts, jogging or on roller skates, dipping and spinning along the sidewalks with disco music blaring from their headphone radios.

One Sunday, soon after Graham could get about, he and Susan went to the Esplanade for a picnic with Jocelyn and Justine. When they had finished lunch, they walked along the grassy banks across from the Cambridge boat basin, where flocks of white-winged sailboats swooped along the water. There were people everywhere—couples, young students who jammed into Boston and Cambridge for summer sessions, people laughing, people sleeping, people playing softball and Frisbee with their kids.

Susan watched the throng, momentarily content. It was good to see all the children. There were so many, but how could none of them be Alex?

Jocelyn and Susan had brought Justine and Alex here one Saturday in March, several weeks after Graham had moved out. There had been mounds of melting gray snow on the riverbank, and the children were engrossed in a game that involved racing each other up a small slope and falling over in mud, laughing.

As Susan sat down on a bench, Jocelyn had said, "I asked Alex if he'd like to sleep over tonight, but he said he couldn't. Mommy would be too sad."

"He did?" He was right. The house had seemed so empty without Graham; Susan hadn't been ready to be without Alex, too.

"I told him you'd be fine," said Jocelyn. "I said, 'Mommy has lots of other friends who could keep her company.' He said, 'She'd miss me, though, because I'm her smallest friend.'" Susan had looked across the distance at the children playing.

"I asked him if he misses his father," said Jocelyn, "and he said yes. He said, 'I think about Daddy more than food.'"

Graham now put his arm around Susan's shoulders as they made their way cautiously along the riverbank. She adjusted her stride to match his, and they concentrated on harmonizing their forward motion, together, one damaged beast with a gravely modified horizon. Once they looked at each other at the same moment and smiled; then they turned their attention to clearing a path for a little boy who wobbled rapidly toward them, his face anxious and joyous on a brand-new two-wheeler.

EXCEPT for the rib belt he still wore, Graham was nearly back to normal, at least physically. It was true, however, that he no longer believed Alex was alive. Not that being beaten up proved anything, but in the month's work of healing his body, the gingerly caution and the slowly diminishing ache, he had imperceptibly healed over the source of his hope. Although this had not been stated between him and Susan, she knew it, and it made her edgy, as if he were a cuckoo in her nest.

Nobody ever said, exactly, that the police department was giving up on Alex. In mid-July there had still been five or six detectives who were in fairly constant touch with Susan. But one by one they were unavailable when she called. By the end of August, there was only Menetti and a sergeant named Laughlin who kept her informed of any tips or leads. These were down to a few dozen a week, from hundreds a day in the beginning.

Susan had been to the Fourth District headquarters once that month to ask them in person to increase the manpower in her search. The building, incongruous on desolate Warren Avenue, had a massive gray cut-stone façade.

The detectives' offices lined a narrow hallway that ran the length of the second floor. Susan found Menetti's office at the top of the stairs. It was a corner office with two desks, a lot of scarred wooden chairs, and posters of Alex on every wall. It was empty. Susan walked on down the hall, passing small, cheerless rooms on either side where detectives smoked cigarettes and plied their trade. She recognized many of the officers. One by one they spoke to her or gave a nod of recognition. She waited nearly half an hour before she got to speak to the head of the department, Lieutenant Bennet. He was a tall, gray-haired man. Offering her a chair, he asked what he could do for her.

"Well," she said, "there doesn't seem to be anyone working on my case. I haven't even seen Al Menetti all week."

"Your case is very important to us," he said. "Every man in this department is ready to drop what he's doing and follow any lead we get if there's any chance he can help find that little boy. Believe me, I know how you feel."

"If I shoot the next person who says he knows how I feel, would it be justifiable homicide?"

"Okay, okay," said Bennet. He gazed at her paternally. "But

I've been in this business a long time. I do know how you feel."

"Being in the business is not the same thing as losing your son!"

"Maybe not," Bennet said blandly as he shifted in his chair. "But I still know more about this business than you do. We are following every lead we get. If we have anything promising to track down, this whole department will be at your service."

Susan was sitting very straight on her chair. "And who is the judge of what is promising?" Her voice trembled.

Bennet stood and smiled. "I know how you feel," he repeated deliberately, "and we will continue to bend all our efforts to solve this case. It has our very top priority. I'll see that Lieutenant Menetti stays in close touch with you."

Quivering with emotion, Susan left the office.

Menetti called her early in the afternoon.

"He as much as said they have no one looking for Alex because there are no leads at all, so let's give up!" she yelled at him.

"It's not true. I swear to you," said Al. "There are two of us assigned to Alex full time, and six others who spend part of every day on it."

"But I haven't even seen you for a week!"

"I was checking on some things. Believe me, nothing has changed. We're looking for him the best we know how."

"Well, then, Al . . . tell me, what should I be doing to keep up the pressure? Do the talk shows help?"

He paused before answering. "It's hard to say. We get a lot more calls when there's publicity. None of them have been adding up to anything, but you never know."

"I see," she said, and surprised herself with the sneering tone in her voice. "Meaning," she said, correcting her tone, "that it makes more work without actually helping."

"You never know what it will stir up," he said. "Look, don't worry about it. Do whatever you feel you can handle."

For a week after this conversation Menetti was there every morning at eight thirty, walking the street from Susan's door around the corner onto Beacon. He'd look up at her window as he got out of the car. If she was there, he'd nod.

Susan now had her public manner pat. When she saw an acquaintance on the street, she took control of the situation so there was no awkwardness.

"Alma," she'd call. "Hello. I haven't seen you in a couple of weeks. Isn't the weather filthy? Poor Taxi's nearly cooked, aren't you, fur person? Have a good afternoon." And off she'd go with a smile.

She called the English Department and arranged her course schedule for the coming year: a general lecture course in the American novel, an honors seminar on Willa Cather, and another on twentieth-century southern fiction.

She agreed to an interview with Charlotte Mayhew, a writer from *Mother's Day* in New York, for a story that would ask the readers to join the hunt for Alex. She spent several evenings arranging all her photographs of Alex from his birth to the time he disappeared. She hoped the magazine would use a couple of pages of them, arranged to look like the pages of a family album.

She had taken to rising very early. She had trouble sleeping more than four or five hours a night, and besides, they often got crank calls in the early hours of the morning. At seven one morning when Susan came in from a walk she went up to Alex's room, taking care not to creak the stairs and wake Graham. In Alex's room she placed one of his baby chairs at the closet so she could step up and reach the shelf where she had put away his sweaters in the spring. These she brought down. On a back hook she found Alex's favorite jacket, made of blue cotton with black knit ribbing at the waist and cuffs. When she slipped her hand into one of its pockets, she touched a squash ball and a little nest of rubber bands. She stood tingling with the most intense recall of her son she had felt in months. It was like holding his hand.

"Are you putting his clothes away?" Graham stood sleepily in the doorway. She started when he spoke.

"No," she said, "getting out his fall things."

"Oh," said Graham after a long pause. He went into the bathroom and shut the door.

ROBERT HAD RENTED A HOUSE IN Nantucket for August, and he invited his parents and Susan and Graham to come for Labor Day. Graham wanted them to go.

"It's the big party weekend. Robert will want us to go to a yacht club dance dressed as chickens," said Susan.

"Well, we won't," said Graham, putting his arms around her. "We'll go sailing by ourselves, and we'll eat a lot of steamers, and we'll sleep in the sun."

"Do you really want to go?" she asked.

"I think Mother and Dad would like to see us."

"I know. They would."

"And I hate to turn Robert down. He sounded lonely."

"Well," she said.

"And I'm lonely, too." She immediately felt this remark as from his whole body, warm against her, and she felt a twinge of panic that turned to resentment as it reached her consciousness.

"Okay," she said, turning from him. "I guess it will be okay."

The evening before they were to leave, the phone rang while Susan was packing. Graham answered it in the kitchen.

"Who is this?" she heard him say. She put down the clothes she was folding and went to the top of the stairs.

"Where in Toronto? . . . Why didn't you call us before?" She went quickly into the bedroom and picked up the extension.

"I'm on the upstairs phone, Graham. This is Mrs. Selky."

The voice on the other end, young, husky, and nervous, said, "Oh, hello," and started again.

It was a woman in Toronto; her sister, she said, lived down the hall from a young couple who'd been trying for years to adopt a baby. This June they had suddenly turned up with a nice bright six-year-old boy who bore a powerful resemblance to Alex.

"Did you call the Toronto police?" Graham asked.

No, she hadn't. She'd only seen the boy three times, and her sister said, "Don't be ridiculous. They got tired of waiting for an infant and adopted an older child. They're a lovely couple." But if he's such a nice bright child, why wouldn't he have been adopted before? Healthy white children were in great demand.

"How do you know he's so healthy and bright?" asked Susan.

The woman had talked to him. She stopped him in the hall one day last week and had a long talk with him. "He said his name was Ronny. I asked him if he'd ever lived in Boston, but he said he didn't think so. Then the mother came along and she didn't look at all pleased. She rushed him off into the apartment."

"But why did you wait so long?" Graham asked again. "Why didn't you call us the first time you saw him?"

"My sister mentioned on the phone tonight that the family is moving to California. I didn't tell my sister I was going to call you." Would she give her name and address? She would rather not. She gave the name and address of the couple with the little boy; then she said she was sorry and she hung up.

Susan ran down the stairs. Graham was sitting with his chin on his hand, staring at the phone.

"What do you think?" she asked.

He didn't look up. "I don't know. What do you think?"

"I think I ought to call Al."

"That's what I thought you were going to say."

She looked at Graham sharply, but he wasn't looking at her.

PAT and the children were already in the car when the phone rang. Al only heard it because he'd gone back for some clothesline with which to tie his suitcase to the roof of the car. When he came out without the clothesline and walked around to Pat's window on the passenger side, she said, "Let me guess. That was Susan Selky, and we're not going to the Cape."

"I'm sorry," he said. "Listen, you go ahead. I'll join you as soon as I can. Maybe I can get there for tomorrow night."

In the back seat the kids had stopped chattering and shoving each other, and now Eugene wailed, "Daddy!"

"Pat, I'm sorry. Something came up, and that's life, okay? I'll get there as soon as I can."

Pat slid over to the driver's side. She started the car. "Al? I would like this to be the last time this happens for a while. This has not been a lovely summer."

"One way or the other, I don't think this case will go on much longer."

"Okay," she said to the back seat, "who gets to ride up here with me? I'm thinking of a number from one to ten. . . ."

He watched how she backed out of the driveway, and hoped she'd slow down once she was out of sight.

WHEN Susan hung up from calling Al, Graham was still not looking at her. "Well?" he said.

"Al agreed that we couldn't not check it out, and he said he'd get right to work."

"And what about us?" asked Graham. "You didn't give him Robert's number in Nantucket. Does that mean we're not going?"

"Well, Graham, what if they need us to identify him? What if we were fogged in and it took us days to get back?"

"Susan, what did Al think the odds were that this would be Alex? How many leads like this have they tracked down so far?"

She looked at him stubbornly.

"I think we should go to Nantucket," he said.

"And do what? Sit by the phone all weekend out there?"

"I think we should go to Nantucket, Susan, and go sailing and eat steamers. I think we should decide to live."

"As in live it up? Goodness, Graham, don't let me keep you. Maybe Robert has party streamers and funny hats."

He looked at her hard. "If not now, then when? If you don't come this time, will you next time?"

"I don't know."

"How long will we let it go on, Susan? The rest of our lives?"

"*I don't know!*"

"Well, I'm going to Nantucket tomorrow morning. I'd like you to go with me."

"And if I don't?"

They looked at each other with long, steady stares.

"I don't know," he said finally.

"Well, I guess we'll see," she said.

So he went to Nantucket by himself, and Susan spent a long,

nearly silent weekend in the deserted city. She sat quietly in the house, dark by contrast to the light outside, waiting for the phone to ring. It wasn't until twilight Saturday that Al called. "I'm sorry," he said. "It looks legit. The couple haven't been out of Canada since last summer, and they have the boy's birth certificate and all the adoption papers in order. The boy does look like Alex. But does Alex speak any French?"

"No."

"This boy is bilingual."

Something beneath her rib cage leaped and tore. These slams of pain were so physical, Susan wondered if it were possible to go on taking them without the inner fibers beginning to shiver apart, like a wooden boat breaking up in a storm.

"Oh," she said. "Well, I suppose I should be getting used to this." But not only was she not getting used to it, it was getting worse instead of better. She tried to reach Graham in Nantucket, but the phone in Robert's house rang and rang and rang with that particular tinny summer-house sound.

On Sunday afternoon she dialed Philippe's number. He answered after the third ring, and he sounded very absent.

"I'm sorry, did I wake you? It's Susan."

"Susan. Oh, no, that's all right. Is anything the matter?"

"No, not at all. I'm sorry if I disturbed you. It just occurred to me you never said if you went to that channel person to ask the spirit about Alex."

"Oh," Philippe said. "Yes, I went. It was peculiar."

"Do you have a minute to tell me about it?"

"Sure, Susan. Just hold on a second." After a brief silence he was back. "Well, it was in this big apartment over in the Fenway. We all sat on cushions on the floor, and after we meditated for a while, people started to ask questions. So I asked if Yasha knew what had happened to Alex, and he thought about it and then he said, 'The earth weeps.' That's all he would say."

"Oh," said Susan.

"But don't be depressed. Yasha says that all the time. He isn't interested in human affairs. He's mainly interested in what a mess

99

we're making of the planet, so when you ask him a question that he thinks is too specific, he just says, 'The earth weeps.'"

"I see," said Susan. "Well, I just remembered you hadn't told me how that came out. I'm sorry if I bothered you."

"No, that's all right. I'll see you on Tuesday."

She did not, however, see him on Tuesday. On Monday evening of Labor Day weekend Philippe was arrested for soliciting a minor.

It was an evening that had a hint of fall coolness in it, and before Philippe had left his apartment, he put on a jacket he had not worn since spring. He was wearing it when the Vice Squad picked him up on Boylston Street. In the jacket pocket the police found a slashed and bloodstained pair of boy's underpants. In the waistband was a name tape that said ALEX SELKY.

THE phone on the nightstand by Susan's bed was an instrument, not a tool as a chisel is the tool of a sculptor, but as a prophet is an instrument of God. When she opened her heart to hope or pray, she often stared at the telephone, as if her grain of faith could press through the wires to expand outward and make itself felt. Bring my boy back. Bring my boy back.

On the morning of Tuesday, September 2, a little after dawn, the telephone elected to bring her the information that Henry Sullivan, known to her as Philippe Lucienne, had been arrested and formally charged with the crime of kidnapping in the first degree, for the theft and presumably the murder of her son, Alexander Graham Selky, Jr. The afternoon paper carried the full story. POLICE BREAK SELKY CASE, ran the headline.

The story read:

Police announced this morning that they have arrested a suspect in the case that has baffled the city, the disappearance of six-year-old Alexander Selky a block from his home in Back Bay on May 15 of this year. Arrested today is Henry Sullivan, 42, a self-confessed homosexual and a convicted child molester who has worked as a houseboy in the Selky home for over two years. Police say that although Sullivan, who calls himself Philippe Lucienne, passed a lie-detector test in the days just after the boy's disappearance, he has been under close observation for several weeks.

Detective Albert Menetti, whose dedication to the solving of this mystery is likely to win him high commendation from the department, explained this morning, "I suspected from the beginning that the kidnapper had to be someone the boy knew. Everything pointed to that, but it was only after weeks of checking police records from all over the country that we discovered Sullivan's true identity and previous record. At that time we began to recheck his alibi for the day of May 15 and those following, and when we found a number of serious discrepancies, the decision was made to put him under surveillance."

The trail that led to Sullivan's arrest began with the discovery that he had served eighteen months in prison in Salt Lake City, Utah, in 1959 for impairing the morals of a minor.

Evidence began to mount when police discovered that a neighbor of John Murchison's, a wealthy art dealer who used Sullivan's services as a housecleaner, saw Sullivan repeatedly enter Murchison's lavish duplex apartment on Beacon Hill during the days immediately following the Selky boy's disappearance. She was aware that Murchison was away in Europe for the week.

The neighbor, whose information has been corroborated by others on the block, said that at one point Sullivan arrived carrying groceries and that during the nights in question there were sometimes loud noises coming from the apartment that could have been part of a scuffle or struggle.

On the night before Murchison was to return, the neighbor, whom police have not identified, apparently heard screams and loud noises coming from the master bathroom area. Late that evening Sullivan was seen leaving the apartment carrying two large plastic garbage bags.

Police admit that up until last night their case against Sullivan seemed to be at a stalemate. Detective Menetti explained, "I have two witnesses who put Sullivan at the scene of the abduction the morning Alex disappeared, although he has sworn he was somewhere else. It would have been a simple matter for Sullivan to persuade the boy to accompany him, since Alex knew and trusted him. The Murchison apartment provided a perfect hideout, but at the end of the weekend, when Murchison was due to return, I believe that the suspect realized that he could neither release the boy nor continue to hold him. At that time I believe that he murdered him and then divided his body between two plastic bags so that neither bag would break when he carried it down the stairs."

The district attorney's office says that it plans to proceed directly to the grand jury, asking for an indictment on the charge of first-degree kidnapping. Under the state penal code, kidnapping in the first degree includes a case in which the person abducted dies during the abduction or before he is able to return to safety. The penalties for this crime are the same as for first-degree murder.

AFTER the first death, there is no other. But Graham and Susan had lost their child so many times. Graham's mourning was ferocious, like a man who walks deliberately into the heart of a storm and opens his coat to it. Susan's grieving instead seemed to be held inside her, as slow-burning hardwood holds the heat. She had lost her son; she had lost her own youth. Within her was something that would never cease to ache. That anguish was all that remained of her son's life.

And God gave His only begotten Son. Yes. Because if the world could not understand God's love as love, it could at least understand the loss of a child, which even to God is the worst the heart can suffer.

The first night after Philippe's arrest Susan dreamed of Alex, the first time in a long time. She had been trying to remember exactly the way his hair fell across his forehead the last night they were together as he sat on the floor of his bedroom in pajamas while she read to him. She could not, but in the dream he was there, walking between her and Graham, holding both their hands. It was spring, and they walked through a park that was mounded high with pink and white azaleas blooming on high green bushes. Susan felt Alex's hand in hers, and her heart glowed as if it were full of sunlight.

Sometime during the second day, Graham looked up at her with an expression close to surprise and said, "This is going to go on forever, isn't it?"

Susan nodded.

She and Graham were silent and dry-eyed almost the whole time through those first three nights and days.

TJ and Annie came, Susan's father and stepmother came, Robert and Graham's parents came. Then, once they got there, nobody knew what to do. The press was encamped on the front steps, so that neither Graham nor Susan could leave the house. Margaret Mayo went in and out to buy food for them all. She brought in the newspapers, and on the fourth day she insisted that Susan read them. By then Philippe had been indicted and arraigned and was being held at the Charles Street jail.

Everyone sat around and tried not to talk about what they were thinking. There were no set mealtimes, just platters of cold food on the dining-room table that Margaret refilled from time to time. The gathering had the air of a wake without a funeral.

Graham's father grew restless and kept getting up and walking around the room as if he were looking for something. Finally he strode over and turned the TV set on. He watched a rerun of "Hollywood Squares," and then came the noon newscast.

"Good afternoon," said the announcer. "Cleanup efforts continue around the metropolitan area in the wake of high winds and record-breaking rains. Damage has been estimated in the millions of dollars, with heavy flooding in many parts of the state."

"The earth weeps," Susan said bleakly to Graham. Then she remembered that he didn't know the joke. Who did? Philippe.

Philippe appeared on the screen, walking between two huge uniformed policemen. His hands were handcuffed in front of him. He made no attempt to duck or hide his head from the cameras; rather, at one point Susan had the impression that he had looked straight through the camera at her. As he appeared, a swarm of reporters surged toward him like bugs on a cake crumb, and you could hear them shouting questions at him. "Mr. Sullivan, Mr. Sullivan! How do you feel?" "We understand that you pleaded innocent." "What are you going to say to Mrs. Selky?"

Without uttering a word, Philippe made his way through them and got into the waiting police car.

The announcer's voice was saying, "This was the scene a few minutes ago on the steps of the Suffolk County courthouse, where Henry Sullivan, the alleged murderer of little Alexander Selky, has just been arraigned on a charge of first-degree kidnapping. As you can see, Mr. Sullivan would not speak to the reporters who have been waiting here hoping to get a word with him. There was a near riot after his departure, as angry demonstrators attacked a small group of gay activists."

At that moment the picture took several zags and pointed toward the sky as the announcer explained that the cameraman had been knocked down in the melee. The shot changed to a view of Susan's front door, apparently being taken live about twenty feet from where the family sat.

The announcer was saying, "And at the house where little Alex Selky lived, the family is still in seclusion. The only statement so far has come from a family friend, Margaret Mayo." The door on the screen opened, and they watched a rerun of Margaret stepping out and stopping on the front step. Her straight iron-colored hair sat on her head like a helmet, and she faced lights and waited calmly for the questions to stop being flung at her. "Mrs. Mayo, how is the family?" "Have they spoken to Henry Sullivan?" "Did you have any idea he was under suspicion?" "Did Mrs. Selky?" "Are they going to give a statement?"

"Well," she said when there was a lull, "I have something to share with you, but I have no intention of shouting." There was relative quiet, although no pause in the flashing of camera bulbs. She said, "Two hundred years ago, when a family suffered as this one has, straw would be put down in front of the house to deaden the sound of wheels, and horses' hoofs would be muffled before they entered the streets. No one expects such a show of civility now, but this family has lost enough. It would be good of you to allow them to mourn in private." There was a brief silence, during which Margaret made her way down the steps.

"Wish I'd done that," said Susan's father.

Susan had to go out sometime, but she physically shrank from it. At last she made herself walk out the door behaving as Margaret had. She tried to hold herself like Margaret, and to wear Margaret's imperturbable expression. When she opened the door, there was a howl of questions from the waiting reporters. She started down the steps, and one reporter actually caught her by the arm as he shouted something at her. She looked at him with patient eyes. She looked down at the hand on her arm; she looked back at him. The hand dropped. She walked on down the steps and gained the sidewalk. Then she walked away. After two days of this the group finally disappeared.

Susan deeply dreaded her first day of teaching again. Every step she took in the direction of a normal life was a step away from her lost child. In the early morning of the first day of classes she had a dream that when she started her lecture, she couldn't hear her own voice. Instead she heard Alex crying.

Graham's first lecture of the term was the same morning as hers. She knew he hadn't slept well, either. But when he had had his coffee, he said, "I'm glad it's here. I'm glad to have something to do." He kissed her on the cheek and wished her luck.

She was looking over her notes from the opening lecture for last year when TJ walked in the door.

"Oh," she said. "Graham's already left."

"I know. This is the neighborhood escort service."

"Ah." She went through the notes one more time while TJ sat down at the edge of a chair and waited. He kept his car keys dangling in his hand.

"TJ, I really don't want to do this."

"But you're going to," he said.

"At least you can't say I should do it because Alex would have wanted me to. Alex would have wanted me to stay at home."

"You're going to do it for yourself," he said.

"Oh, TJ, imagine having no reason but myself to do anything."

He saw the panic beginning. "Come on," he said. "Move."

ONE afternoon about a week after classes had begun, Susan found a tall man with an astonishingly round head waiting for her in the hall outside the room where she held her seminar. "Mrs. Selky," he said, walking beside her as she started down the hall. "I'm Lesley George. I'm Henry's attorney."

"Henry?" She stopped.

"Philippe," he said.

"Oh." She felt a quake of loathing grip her insides, followed by a real fear that she might throw up. This passed quickly. The man's eyes swam behind round wire-rimmed glasses.

"Can I buy you some coffee?" he asked.

"I guess," she said.

"The point is," said the attorney when they were seated in a booth in a nearby restaurant and Susan had ordered tea, "Henry wants to see you."

"Why?"

"To tell you he's not guilty." The round eyes were remarkably ingenuous. "You're the only one he *will* see. He wouldn't talk to the court's psychiatrist. He tried to fire me the first day I met him because I mentioned the idea of an insanity plea."

"I take it you think he did it." She was astounded at the impact of this phrase. "Killed my son" was what "did it" meant.

Lesley George looked thoughtfully at his hands. "I believe he's entitled to the best possible defense. And I believe he stands a good chance of being acquitted. In spite of all the papers are making of it, the prosecution's case is very weak."

Susan's mouth was dry with fear. Her insides felt as if the acid of her tea had tanned them. She simply did not believe she could endure any more ambiguity than she had already. The worst had happened. At least the worst was over.

"If I can keep Henry's Utah conviction out of the record—and

I ought to be able to—what have you got left? There are witnesses who put him on Beacon Street the morning your boy disappeared, and that's bad, because he lied to the police about that. The odd thing is, he passed the lie-detector test they gave him in the beginning. He's failed two in a row since he was arrested, but I can keep all that out of the record. Frightened subject. Prejudiced interpretation of the test. That sort of thing."

"What about motive?" Susan whispered.

The lawyer waved his hand. "Don't need a motive in a sex case. Sex is a universal motive. Of course, in Henry's case, his . . . um, particular predilections will weigh heavily with a jury."

"And what about the . . . Alex's . . . in his pocket?"

This time Lesley George looked directly at her. "Henry can explain that," he said. "The blood type on the pants is O-positive. Very common. It's your son's type, and it's also Henry's. He can explain a lot of things. Well enough to create reasonable doubt."

Susan felt a creeping horror as the ambiguity made itself part of her. Was he telling her that Alex was alive and an innocent man was going to be tried for doing something that might not have happened at all? Or was he saying that the man who murdered her son stood a very good chance of going free?

"I'll see him," she said.

"Well, good. I'll arrange it."

THE room in which Susan waited for Henry Sullivan was walled with large turquoise tiles, like a school cafeteria. There were high windows covered with heavy wire, through which slanted bright bars of light jailed behind crisscrossed shadows. A guard sat at a big bare desk with a telephone on it.

Philippe was led in between two guards wearing blue shirts and pistols on their hips. He sat down at a table across from Susan. They looked into each other's eyes for what seemed a long time. Hypocrite is what came into her head. His eyes were bald blue, with gray radial glints around the pupil like spokes on a wheel. Do you not flinch because you are innocent? she asked the eyes, or because you are so guilty?

"Shall I call you Philippe or Henry?" She spoke first.

"Henry."

That surprised her. She also caught, a beat later, that he hadn't pulled the vowel the way Philippe would have. Heeenry. "You wanted to see me?" she asked.

He nodded. "Susan," he said, "I am guilty of a great many things. I am, as my stepfather would say, a screaming queer. But I have never in my life knowingly hurt another person, and I did not, ever, in any way hurt Alex."

Their faces were matched in blankness as they faced each other across the table, like Man and Death playing chess.

"You lied about being on Beacon Street the morning Alex disappeared."

"No," he said. "I didn't."

"You failed a lie-detector test about it. Twice."

"Susan, I was scared."

"How do you explain two people who say they saw you there?"

"I can't. Error. Mistaken identity. Take your pick."

"What were you doing at Murchison's that weekend if you didn't have Alex hidden there?"

"If you met somebody you liked and you lived in a fourth-floor walk-up but you had the keys to a duplex apartment with an owner in Europe, what would you do?"

She looked at him levelly. "What about what you had in your pocket?" She didn't want to hear the answer. She was afraid she would not believe him and afraid that she would. Resisting, she felt the old hope stir painfully within her.

He held up his right hand with his palm facing her. There was a scar an inch long from what must have been a deep cut. "At your house. Last spring. I reached into a sinkful of sudsy water and cut my hand on a broken glass. I keep rags for dusting under the sink, and I grabbed one. An old pair of Alex's underpants. I cut them with the kitchen shears and tied the cloth around my hand. I was bleeding all over the place. I started home with the pair of underpants on my hand, but by the time I got to the subway I realized that the bleeding had stopped, so I took the bandage off and put it in my pocket. Then I went on home."

She stared at him. "Did you go somewhere for stitches?"

"I told you, the bleeding stopped."

"I see," she said, though she saw nothing. She was feeling.

WITHOUT a plan, in a suspension of belief and disbelief, Susan found herself again on Warren Avenue, on her way to Menetti's office. She walked up the stairs to the second floor slowly. Before she turned into his office, she had a sudden intuition of what she would see, and she was right.

Inside, the posters of Alex were all gone. On the bulletin board facing the door was a new poster with a police sketch of a young man who had raped two young girls. WANTED, said the poster. HAVE YOU SEEN THIS MAN?

It was the first time Susan had seen Menetti since Philippe's arrest. He met her with a look of very great sorrow in his eyes. "Come in," he said, and led her into his office. He sat down at his desk, and she sat on a straight-backed chair facing him.

"How are you?" he asked sympathetically.

"I've been to see Philippe," she said.

Menetti sighed. "Never in my life," he said, "have I hoped so much that I was wrong about a case."

"I think you are," said Susan.

"Excuse me?" Menetti had a pretty good idea that he was about to be promoted. He'd been on the news every day for a week. He'd gotten in the rhythm of modestly dismissing his contribution to solving the mystery.

"I think you made a mistake, Al. I don't think he did it."

"Well," he said gently, "I guess I can understand that. He is very persuasive. That's part of the DA's case against him."

"Al, have you talked to him?"

"Of course I've talked to him."

"Did you give him a chance to explain?"

"Look, the case is out of my hands now. My department only handles a case up till the time that we discover for certain that a crime has been committed. Philippe was arrested by Vice, and

109

the case against him, that's handled by Homicide. Of course they keep me informed."

"Have you heard his explanation?"

"Wait here a minute," said Al. "I'll be right back." He got up and strode out, looking annoyed. In a minute he returned and sat back down in his chair. He dropped some papers on the desk. "I want you to follow me carefully," he said. "We've got a very strong case against Sullivan, believe me, and it is not going to be tried in the newspapers before a jury is impaneled, so—"

"What evidence do you have? Besides the underpants?"

Menetti looked exasperated. "I'm sorry," he said, "but that's just none of your business."

"Oh, really."

"Excuse me. I'm sorry. What I meant to say was, the prisoner has a right to a fair trial, and the people have a right to a fair trial against him. There's a gag order on the department, and I'm not going to tell you or the press any more. But look, now. This is a copy of the psychiatrist's record from the court in Utah. I'll read you the conclusion. 'It is the examiner's opinion that the prisoner is a psychopathic personality. He has clear homosexual drives and a predisposition to commit sexual crimes that make him a menace to society. It is recommended that he be confined in an institution suitable for the care and treatment of his disorder.'"

Menetti laid down the papers and looked at Susan. Her eyes were fixed on his as if they were boring tools.

"Now *listen*," he said, losing his temper. "*I have done all I can for you.* It's over. You'll just have to accept that."

"If you're wrong, and I'm right, then my son's still missing."

He stood up. "You'll have to talk to Homicide, and I've already told you that they can't tell you any more than I have."

"Who are the witnesses who saw Philippe the morning Alex disappeared? Why didn't I ever hear about them?"

"I'm sorry. There is nothing more I can do for you."

Susan gazed at him steadily for a long moment. When he looked so uncomfortable that she thought the moment would stay with him, she rose slowly and left.

IN THE LIVING ROOM THE CLOCK ON the mantel over the fireplace ticked softly. Graham sat at his desk in the corner, working quietly on his Milton book. Susan noticed how he sat. No twitching, no twisting a lock of hair, no tapping a pencil. His grief seemed to have coursed through him in one galling dose, leaving behind only this fiercely determined stillness. Somewhere upstairs, at the evening bathtime, storytime, an idle creak reminded her that there was nothing human moving up there.

"Graham," she said. He held up a hand to indicate that he wanted a moment more before being interrupted. Oh, the stillness. No more drilling clamor of the telephone. No meandering friendly chat between them. As much of the future as they cared to contemplate was tomorrow, and they had more than enough reason to avoid the past. The present, without inflection or implication, was all, and they floated in it quietly, side by side.

"Okay," said Graham. He turned his head to her without turning in his chair.

"I went to see Philippe today. His lawyer asked me to."

Now he put down his pen and turned to face her. "Well," he said. He wasn't asking, but he was going to have to hear.

"He wanted to tell me that he didn't kill Alex."

"Yes, I'm sure he wanted to tell you that." Graham looked at her stolidly.

"I think it's true," said Susan.

Graham just looked at her. She could see his eyes flick over her, out at the night, and back to her.

He said, "No."

"What do you mean, no?"

He stood up from his desk and carefully pushed in his chair. Towering over her, he said, much louder, "No . . . no . . . no! No more." He left the room and went upstairs, and she sat looking after him, stunned.

She sat for some time listening to him move around. What was he doing? Not getting ready for bed. Looking for something? What? Finally she recognized the rhythm of his footsteps. He was packing. There he went into the bathroom for his shaving things; there he was checking the dresser drawers to see what he forgot; there he was closing the suitcase. There he was walking into Alex's room and standing in the darkness for a long time.

She heard the suitcase bump against the banister as he came down the stairs. He set it down in the kitchen and came into the living room. He looked at her once, with an unreadable expression; then he went over to his desk, opened his briefcase, and began packing his papers. What was he challenging her to say? Yes, I believe it's over; yes, I want to forget I had a son? Have a son? Yes, I surrender Alex so I can love you?

No.

At last he closed the briefcase and turned to look at her. His eyes were filled with a dense, beaten, challenging stare.

She said only, "Where would I reach you, if I needed to?"

He said harshly, "At Naomi's."

He was out the door when she suddenly ran to the top of the stairs and called down after him, "Wait a minute. Don't you even have to call her to tell her you're coming?" He shook his head, glaring, and she could see him holding his downcurved lips together to keep in the tears.

Susan put in a call to Charlotte Mayhew at *Mother's Day* in New York.

"She's in a meeting," said her secretary. "Can I tell her what this is in reference to?" Charlotte Mayhew had spent some ten hours in Susan's house less than a month ago, taping interviews and preparing an article on Alex to be entitled "Have You Seen This Child?" She had the scrapbook Susan had made up, containing almost all of her photographs of Alex.

"It's in reference to an article she's writing," said Susan. She had to keep calling for three days before Charlotte called back.

"Susan," said the arch, maternal voice. "I haven't had a minute to return your call, but you've been on my mind. How *are* you?"

"Fine," said Susan.

"I'm sure you're wanting the photographs back. I'll send them airmail special. Give me the address again."

"Charlotte, I wanted to talk to you about the article. Could we meet? I'd be glad to take the shuttle down."

"Oh, *yes*. Let's do lunch; just let me check my calendar. . . . Oh, isn't this disgusting. Do you know, I don't have a lunch open for the next two weeks?"

"But, Charlotte, I don't care about lunch. I'd just like to talk to you soon about the article."

"Well, honey, I'm afraid the thrust of the article was the inspirational approach, your faith and your courage . . . plus the appeal to the readers themselves, the idea that they could *help*. That's how I sold it to the editorial board."

Susan thought of the phone calls from this woman last July to the effect that the editors of *Mother's Day* felt that Susan's story was the story of the decade.

"But, Charlotte, I don't feel that the nature of the story has changed. I'm convinced that the police have made a mistake." She paused to hear Charlotte's reaction to this bombshell, but there was judicious silence at the other end of the line.

"Yes," Susan said. "I've talked to Henry Sullivan, and I believe that in all good faith the police have made a mistake. A tragic mistake," she added, suddenly seeing the headline as *Mother's Day* would write it. "Don't you see? Nothing has changed. Alex may still be out there, missing me, but because the police have made this terrible mistake, not only is an innocent man in grave danger, but so is Alex and so am I and so are all our hopes. Charlotte, if I'm right, don't you see what it means?"

Susan finally stopped talking. A silent beat or two.

"I *do* see," said Charlotte emphatically. "I see exactly. But to be honest, this just isn't a *Mother's Day* story. We actually have a list of no-noes, and I'm afraid anything about homosexuals . . . you understand, as far as we're concerned we don't know they exist. Pathetic, isn't it? But that's what I'm up against. There just isn't any way I could write the story that would make it right for

Mother's Day. I'm sure somebody will do a bang-up job of it, and I'm sorry it won't be us. Now, lambie . . ."

"Good-by, Charlotte," said Susan.

SUSAN continued to teach her classes, working mechanically from last year's notes. But there were times, more and more often, when she thought of giving up out of sheer loneliness. One night a new faculty couple on a one-year fellowship from Israel invited her on the spur of the moment to join them and a few friends for dinner. The talk over drinks was lively and trivial, and Susan was keenly aware of how long it had been since she'd been with people who were just enjoying themselves. The evening was an escape back into the lost world of the ordinary, until just before supper was served, when the hostess brought in her little six-month-old daughter in her pink terry-cloth stretch suit to be kissed good night.

The women each took a turn holding her, and for Susan the warm fragrant weight of the baby against her breast brought back a deeply held memory that gave her profound pleasure.

"She's a real dream," Susan said to the young mother when she came back from putting her baby in the crib.

The mother nodded shyly. "I worry about her all day long. So many things can happen to babies, crib death, accidents . . . I won't leave her outside in the sun in her carriage; I'm afraid someone will steal her."

Here her husband joined in, laughing. "There are thousands of babies in Boston, but ours is so perfect that gangs of criminals are plotting to steal her away from us."

The mother said softly and earnestly, "But things do happen to babies. If something did, I know I would kill myself."

"Why do you say that?" asked Susan sharply. "Is that what you think you *should* do?"

The young woman looked at her in surprise.

"Do you have children?" one of the other guests asked Susan.

"Yes," she replied vehemently, and then, realizing that she could not answer any specific questions about her child without spoiling the evening, she contradicted herself and said, "No."

By that time it was clear to everyone that Susan was reacting to a rather ordinary situation with uncommon emotion. When conversation resumed, it had lost its spontaneous drift, so Susan apologized and excused herself early.

That night for the first time she understood why some parents who have lost children move and start a new life among strangers. But how could she go away? How could she, ever? This was where Alex knew to find her. This was where he would try to come home.

In the long, still hours of her days Susan established new rules and rhythms to replace the events of her former life. She made herself cook at least one recognizable meal a day and not eat it standing up at the sink. Every evening at eleven she took a mug of hot mint tea up to bed with her. If she could keep her entire attention confined to the pages of her book as she lay in bed and sipped the tea, she could usually go to sleep by midnight.

In her inner life, there were two things she had rules about. One was If Only. If Only I had walked with him that morning. If Only he'd left a minute earlier, or later. If Only I'd called him back for his jacket. . . . She could bear to imagine almost any of the possible fates that Alex had met. She could not bear It Might Not Have Happened.

The other thing was imagining how he would come back. At first she had thought the phone would ring. She would pick it up and there would be his voice. "Hello, Mommy?" Perhaps she still believed that, for a millisecond, each time the phone rang, even now. But the phone rang so often, and dreams replayed too many times lose their power to move.

After that she'd decided that the way it would happen would be through Menetti. He'd call to say they were checking out a lead. They'd received a call from a schoolteacher in Florida who'd recognized the new little boy in first grade. Then there would be wrenching hours of waiting and pacing, and then Menetti would call to say that Alex was on a plane home. The scene at the airport. The press. Graham. The explosion of joy in her heart.

And the look in Menetti's eyes as he gave her back her son. Well . . . that one was gone now.

But there were still ways it would happen. She allowed herself to develop only one at a time, and she allowed herself to think of it only in the hour before sleep, when she turned out the light. For instance, someone would see a picture in an old magazine at the hairdresser's and recognize the little "grandchild" of the people down the block. Or, a couple from the neighborhood would pass a schoolyard one day and see a little boy playing alone. They would recognize the face on the poster, even though his hair would be dyed and his missing tooth grown in, because no one, no one, could mistake that brilliant smile. They would call the police, or they would simply drive up to her door one day and ring the bell. . . .

Lord, I believe; help thou mine unbelief.

THE posters of Alex, the ones that said STILL MISSING, had nearly all been taken down. Susan had new ones printed up using a different photograph, another way of seeing his face, and in the evenings and on weekends she would walk around the neighborhood asking permission to post them. She preferred to put them in storefronts, where they could be seen through the glass but not harmed by the weather or defaced. Recently on the subway she had seen one of the old posters with Alex's face drawn over with a felt-tip pen to look like a minstrel show pickaninny.

Often now when she showed a store owner the new poster, he would look at her oddly and say, "I heard they solved that; the kid was murdered by some queer."

"No, it was a mistake," she'd say.

"Oh. I guess, go ahead and put it up," he would say.

But the owner of a deli in Kenmore Square, thinking Susan was another of the volunteers, said, "Hey, honey, give me a break. People want to come in here and eat without feeling like they should lose their appetite from sympathy. Somebody should tell the parents, enough is enough."

"Thank you so much," said Susan.

One chilly Sunday morning in mid-October Jocelyn appeared at Susan's door carrying a bag of bagels and a copy of the *Globe*. "Justine's at a friend's, and I said to myself, This is *too* nice a morning to be having breakfast alone. So here I am."

"I'm delighted," said Susan. She put on a pot of fresh coffee and, from the refrigerator, produced orange juice and butter. On a shelf, in the back, she found a jar of jam. "Oh-oh. Here's some antique jam. It seems to have fur on it."

"Looks to have been there since Alex," said Jocelyn.

Susan looked at her warily. "Yes, probably," she agreed.

When the coffee was ready, they sat at the dining table in the sunlight and read the paper. It was like old times, except that in old times the children would have been playing upstairs.

"Feel like taking a walk?" asked Susan, folding her paper.

"No, thanks," said Jocelyn. "You know you don't take walks, honey; you go on hunts."

"Now, exactly what do you mean by that?"

"Just what I said," answered Jocelyn. "You never go out any-more without studying every little child to see if it's Alex. You look down every alley and peek into people's windows. . . . I can't sit by any longer and watch you do this to yourself."

Susan got up and carried the breakfast dishes into the kitchen; then she returned to the table and with a deep breath said, "Okay, Jocelyn. Get it off your chest."

"All right, honey." Jocelyn reached across the table and touched Susan's arm. "You're a brave lady," she said. "You've been through a whole lot of pain and you've carried it like a warrior. But it's time to let go. You're only hurting yourself. I know it's none of my business, but your friends are worried about you."

"Really?" said Susan dryly. "Where are they?"

"Look, Susan. There was a time in my life when I was just so unhappy I was making myself and everyone else miserable, and it took someone I loved, getting real tough with me, to help me pull out of it. So, I have to say this because I love you. It's time for you to face facts. Alex is gone, and he's not coming back, and the way you're taking it makes me afraid for you."

"I'm sorry if it's inconvenienced you," said Susan.

"That's all right," said Jocelyn. "Be angry at me. It's a start. That's probably one reason you haven't begun to heal yourself; you're carrying all that anger about what Philippe did inside of you. Susan, you must want to *kill* him."

"I not only don't want to kill him, I want to clear him. I don't think he did anything."

"See, that's what I'm talking about. It scares me to say this, but you're out of touch with reality. If you don't face what's really happened to you, there's going to be no pulling you back."

"If I don't believe what you believe, I'm out of touch with reality?"

"Now, listen. I know you're angry, but I'm trying to help. I just wish you would see my therapist. She's *brilliant*."

"Jocelyn, there is a difference between neurotic pain and real pain. There's a difference between stress over the bags under your eyes and what you feel when your only child is stolen."

After Jocelyn left, Susan threw the jar of moldy jam against the kitchen wall and cried hot tears of annoyance and loneliness as the red clotted mess dripped down the wall.

ON NOVEMBER 3 A SMALL STORY appeared in the Boston *Globe*.
A man named Albert Lipscomb was found living in a cabin in a
small town in West Virginia with two young boys he had abducted. One was nine and one was twelve. The one who was
twelve had never even been reported missing. The other one had
disappeared from a park near his home in Philadelphia over a
year ago and had been written off as a runaway. According to
the news report, the boys had been calling the man Dad, and
even attended school. What had led the police to investigate the
"family" was the curiosity of a country schoolteacher who was
puzzled by the fact that the boys claimed to be brothers, although
one of them was black.

Albert Lipscomb, the paper noted, was a convicted sex of-
fender. He was known to have been in the Boston area in the
spring and had been questioned about the disappearance of Alex
Selky, which was the principal reason the story now made the
Boston papers.

To Susan, it was a sign. The local media woke up and remembered her name. One news show wanted to know if they could
film her phoning the mother in Philadelphia whose little boy had
been found, giving congratulations. Would they run pictures of
Alex? Susan asked. Would they let her explain that she still believed he, too, would be found? They agreed that they would.

It was as if the clock had been turned back. The phone rang,
the reporters called, and the news shows asked her to come on
and talk about how it feels to hope that somewhere in the world
your lost son is alive. She didn't care that they thought she was
deranged. Hope coursed through her like a cleansing fire, and she
was full of energy and fierce conviction.

She called Menetti. Yes, he said, he'd seen the story. No, it
didn't make any difference. They had already questioned Lipscomb at the time; there was no point in doing it again.

MENETTI saw her on the news show. He was in a bar up the
street from police headquarters. On the black-and-white TV set
above the bar she seemed a little thinner than the last time he

saw her. He sipped his draft and watched the deep, steady look in her eyes as she called the woman whose child had come home. The smile on her face, so like the little boy's on the poster, nearly broke his heart. Where was her courage coming from? How long was she going to keep it up?

The traffic was heavy on the expressway when he started for Saugus. It was nearly at a standstill by the time he reached the Mystic River Bridge. He could turn on the radio and listen to one of those helicopter guys who told you where the tie-ups were, but tonight he didn't want the distraction. He was scanning the traffic. His eyes moved ceaselessly. Presently he recognized what he was doing: he was looking for the blue car. Blue 1963 or 1964 Oldsmobile sedan; rust spots on the doors; whitewall tire on the right-front wheel. Systematically, he scanned the slowly moving lanes and asked himself for the thousandth time, How could it happen that that car was never seen again?

IN THE second week of November Philippe tried to kill himself. He was cut down from a bar in his cell from which he had hung himself with a torn bed sheet. Nobody knew how long he'd been there, and the hospital had not yet determined whether or not there had been brain damage. Susan tried to see him at the hospital, but she was refused.

Late one evening she called Graham. "He's not here," said Naomi.

"Naomi," said Susan through tears, "I need to talk to him. I don't know what it means, Philippe trying to die. Does it mean he lied to me? What can't he live with—his guilt? Or his innocence? I don't know who else to talk to. No one else has lost Alex except Graham."

There was a long silence. Finally Naomi said, "All right, Susan. I'll give him the message. But we're trying hard to make a life together here, and I resent you using this situation all the time to get to Graham."

Graham called her back the next morning, but by that time the urge to speak to him had passed.

As THE DAYS GREW SHORTER and the chill in the autumn air deepened, the panes of glass in the living-room windows were covered with thin frost when Susan went with her coffee cup in the early mornings to sit looking down at the street. From the lush gold and blue of the last morning on earth that she had seen her son, the light had changed to the flat gray brightness of impending winter.

He would be so cold now if, by some prayer-answering overlay of time, she could see him once more on this street as she saw him that last morning. If she looked down as she did every morning, and there he simply was, striding out into the new spring day. She could see him so clearly. The lilt of his walk, his sturdy neck and arms, and the flash of sunlight on his dark hair. And every morning, every morning of her life, she saw him reach the corner, turn, and, smiling, wave good-by.

These long, empty days she rarely felt anger or fear or sadness. What she felt was a brimming love for him and no way to give it. There was a dim sensory memory that haunted her—the smell of his skin, the sight of his head pressed against her cheek so close that its outline became the curve of the earth, and the angular feel of limbs, all knees and elbows—that gave a pleasure too complex to recover or yet ever to give up, the deep, unremarkable joy of hugging her child.

IT WAS a slushy gray-bright morning the week after Thanksgiving. When Menetti arrived at the office, he happened to overhear Sergeant Pollard saying into the phone, "I see . . . I see. Yes, well, as I told you, we've closed the file on that case. Yes. It was in all the papers, Mrs. Robbins." He glanced at Menetti, who mouthed at him silently, "Which case?"

"Selky," Pollard mouthed back.

Menetti reached for the phone. "This is Lieutenant Menetti," he said. "Can I help you?"

"I'm calling to help you," said the woman. "I know where that little Selky child is, and I've called twice now to tell you about it. If I were a Massachusetts resident, I'd be pretty concerned about what the police are doing all day. You can't bring home one sad little child."

"Yes, I understand," said Menetti. "Could you give me your name and address, please?"

"I told you already. Malvina Robbins, 4429 Baily Street, Willimantic, Connecticut." As he wrote this down, Menetti saw Sergeant Pollard roll his eyes up at the ceiling. Mrs. Robbins was saying, "I can see the child out my window now marching around in that mush by himself. Why isn't he in school? Tell me that."

"I can't, Mrs. Robbins. You tell me."

"Because he's that stolen child. I did tell you. I knew it when they moved in. The man didn't have no toys for him like a real daddy would."

"How do you know he doesn't have any toys?" Menetti asked.

"I watched them move in! They only got the one suitcase. When I used to go someplace with my kids, it would take a wheelbarrow to bring the toys in."

"Maybe they can't afford toys. Maybe they're poor."

"Poor! He's no more a daddy than the man in the moon."

"And how do you know that, Mrs. Robbins?"

"I know it because I know this is that little stolen child. I got the picture of him from the paper, and also I saw his mother on TV and she showed us another picture. What happened was, when I was reading the paper about this little Boston boy that disappeared, I looked up and there was Jesus, and He said to me, 'Malvina, you better clip that picture. My Father moves in mysterious ways, and it may be that you, Malvina, will be the instrument that will bring the lost little lamb home to his grieving mommy.' And I said to Jesus . . ."

At this point Menetti picked up an eraser from the desk and threw it at Sergeant Pollard. "I see, Mrs. Robbins," he was saying as Pollard, laughing soundlessly, went on about his work.

Now that Malvina Robbins had Menetti's name, she telephoned him on an average of twice a week. He sometimes wondered how she found time to work him in between conversations with Jesus.

In the week after Christmas he'd had to listen to a complete rendition of what the Lord had said to Malvina when He came to share her holiday turkey. (Would you believe that the dear Christ baby had never tasted turkey before in all His life?)

This morning it had taken close to three minutes by the clock for her to pause long enough for Menetti to say into the phone, "Happy New Year to you, too, Malvina."

"I want to know when you'll be coming down here," she was saying, "because after you pick up that little lost child, I want you to bring him by here for milk and cookies. I offered him a plate of my Christmas cookies just the other day, but that man just looked at me with the one straight eye he's got and took that child off by the arm like I was the devil. Won't let him talk to me at all. . . ."

"Malvina," said Menetti, "thank you for calling. I have to go now and make arrangements to come down there. Yes, I'll be in touch very soon about when we're coming, and I'll let you know. It takes time to line up all the squad cars and so on. . . . Yes, Malvina. Thank you. I'll pray for you, too."

Menetti hung up and sank his head in his hands. I'll pray, all right, he thought. I'll pray that the phone company takes your phone out by the roots, you poor nut case.

And in Willimantic, Connecticut, Malvina Robbins hung up her phone and went back to the kitchen window to look out into the next-door yard again. No way she was going to rest until somebody came to rescue that child.

There he was, poor little boy. He was sitting on the concrete step by himself, just staring into the empty yard. There was a layer of gray snow on the ground. In one corner of the yard a broken canvas chair lay against the fence. The little boy wore no mittens. He had laid out a row of little squares of bread, white against the dirty snow, in a neat line. Malvina watched him stare at them until at last a mangy sparrow dropped down, ate one of the chunks, hopped around for a while, then flew off again. After a long pause the boy got up and replaced the sparrow's bread with another little piece; then he sat back down again.

It was the Friday evening of the long Washington's Birthday weekend, and Menetti had arrived home late. Dinner was already over. Pat was angrily washing dishes. Eugene had just rushed upstairs crying and slammed the bedroom door. Before Al could find out what was going on, the phone rang. He grabbed it.

"Hello, Al?"

"Yes, Susan," he said. Pat took her hands out of the soapy water and whirled around and glared at him. Menetti pulled a chair out from the kitchen table and sat down in his overcoat. "How are you?" he said into the phone. He had felt an odd quiver when he heard her voice again after so many weeks.

"Fine. Al, I just got a phone call from this woman in Connecticut. She's called me twice, actually."

Damn it, Menetti said to himself. Malvina. This was where he stopped feeling sorry for the loons out there and started wishing he could just have them rounded up and fitted with straitjackets. It was annoying enough having Malvina on his back, but now she was going to cause real pain.

"She lives in Willimantic," Susan was saying. "She said she's been in touch with you."

"Malvina Robbins, right?"

"Yes."

"Now, Susan—"

"Al." Something in her voice seemed to flood him with awful sadness.

"Susan," he said wearily, "did she tell you about Jesus coming to Christmas dinner? Or how He takes His tea every afternoon? Did she tell you how He used to take two lumps, but now He just takes cream?"

There was a long silence, and Menetti tried to remember how it was he got into the position of adding to Susan's hurt. He knew from her pause that she had heard enough from Malvina to doubt her.

125

Susan started again. "But that doesn't prove there's no boy there. Why isn't a child that age in school, Al?"

Menetti stretched and shook his head. "He could be retarded; he could have a handicap. . . ."

"Or he could be Alex."

Menetti sighed, trying to think of what to say.

"Couldn't he, Al?" she persisted. "Are you so sure that there is not *one* chance left under heaven that it is Alex that you can't even check it out? Can't you just have the police in Willimantic drive by and *look?*"

"No," he said. "I can't. This case is closed, and there is no way I could justify an action like that. I am under very specific orders not to spend any more time on this matter, for the very good reason that we have Henry Sullivan's trial coming up. If it comes out that any member of my department, let alone me, is muddying the waters by looking for the child Henry Sullivan killed, I'd be very surprised if we didn't see the indictment thrown out, and I'd be lucky if I wound up directing traffic. Got it?" He was shouting, and the volume of his voice made him understand how torn he was with pity for her, and guilt.

Susan was silent for another long moment, during which he dreaded her reaction. When it came, her voice sounded a little frightened, but firm.

"I guess I could go to Willimantic myself," she said.

Menetti pictured her going to Malvina's door and felt a spasm of fear. He knew so much better than she how many different kinds of weird a person like Malvina might be. "Look, don't do that, all right?"

"What else can I do?"

"Think it over a little while. Sort out what you want to believe from what's happening. It's a long weekend anyway. Just give yourself the time off, and we'll talk about it Tuesday."

"Give myself time off from what?"

"Susan, I'll talk to you Tuesday."

He hung up the phone and turned wearily to share his sorrow with Pat, only to see from the way she was staring at him that she clearly had a few things she intended to share with him first.

"Susan Selky?" she said coldly.

He shrugged and nodded.

"Not only did you miss dinner again for the fifth time in two weeks, we're going to start with Susan Selky again? We're going to have a replay of last summer, when the kids forgot what you looked like?"

"I haven't talked to her in two months," said Al.

"Did you happen to notice your youngest son, that's the one called Eugene, bawling up the stairs as you graced us with your presence this evening?"

"Yes."

"Did it cross your mind to wonder what was going on before you dived for the telephone? You've spent more time in the last year worrying about a kid who's been dead since May than you have about your own children, you know that?"

Menetti just stared at her. She was in full cry, all right.

"For your information," stormed Pat, "Eugene is crying because I said he could sleep over at Willy's house this weekend, and now he can't because he wet his bed again."

"I see. And I made him do it."

"Very funny. Did you bother to read that article I gave you?"

Al dimly remembered her giving him one of those women's magazines to read, but he hated those magazines. They were all about Jell-O molds and breast cancer.

"If you had read it, you might be able to figure out that when a kid with no medical problem continues to wet his bed, he's probably trying to get attention. Like, for instance, the attention of his father. You haven't spent one whole day alone with Eugene since I brought him home from the hospital. Just because he's the youngest and you've already been through this six times before doesn't mean Eugene has. Remember when Angela was Eugene's age? You used to spend all day Saturday with her."

Al knew it was true. He hardly ever spent time with Eugene, the way he had with the first kids.

"And don't think I want to keep him home. Maryann and the

twins are coming in the morning, and now I don't have anywhere for the babies to sleep."

"Your sister's coming? Why?"

"Because it's the long weekend, that's why!"

"Good," said Al. "Then you won't need me. I'll take Eugene and we'll go off for the day, and you and Maryann can spend the whole day complaining about your mother." He got up and marched up the stairs to hammer on Eugene's door.

"Eugene! Eugene!"

Eugene, who expected to be spanked for wetting his bed, didn't answer.

"Eugene," yelled Al through the door, "how'd you like to spend the day with me tomorrow, buddy? We'll go off somewhere and leave the ladies and the babies to themselves, okay?"

Eugene opened his door and came out, his face still puffy from crying. "Gee, Dad," he said. "Okay."

THEY drove out right after breakfast. Eugene was glowing with pleasure, and it was a while before he asked, "Where we going, Dad?"

It was a bitterly cold day, and though the roads were clear, the yards and sidewalks were piled with snow.

"Gee, I don't know. How about the aquarium?"

"We went there with Mom last week."

Menetti thought awhile. "Well, what do you want to do?"

"I'd like to see your office. I've never been there."

Menetti thought about it. "But, Eugene, your mother would kill me if I went to the office today. Even to show you."

"She would?"

"Yes. She's very mad at me for spending too much time there."

"You're right," said Eugene philosophically. "It's okay, though, Dad," he added. "I just like driving with you."

"Well, fine. I'll tell you what. You can be my deputy, and we'll pretend we're going on a mission."

"Hey, great! Can I have a gun?"

"Sure," said Menetti. "Here." He cocked his thumb and stuck

out his index finger to make a pistol. Eugene solemnly pretended to take it and tuck it into his belt.

They drove for several miles in silence, both feeling highly satisfied. Suddenly Menetti thought, Maybe I can kill two birds with one stone here. After all, I do have to go somewhere. I could let him know what police work is really like.

"Say, Deputy . . ."

"Sir," said Eugene.

"I've got a mission you can help me out with. But it's a very delicate one, and it must be an absolute secret. No talking about it down at headquarters."

"Honestly, Dad?" asked Eugene.

"Absolutely. Do you accept?"

"Yes, sir."

"Okay. First, open the glove compartment and find me the road map marked Southern New England." Eugene did this. "Now open it up." Eugene unfolded the large creased sheet. "Good. See the legend on the side of the map. Try to find a town called Willimantic, under Connecticut."

There was a long silence while the deputy held the map close to his face. "Found it!" he cried finally. He showed his father the map, pointing to Willimantic.

"Route 6, that's what I thought," said Menetti. "Good man!"

Eugene refolded the map with some difficulty. "What do I do next, sir?" he asked.

"You sit."

"How much longer?"

"At least another hour."

"Why do we have to go so far?"

"We are doing one of the jobs that we do often, and that is checking out a crank call. Sometimes we ask for information, and a lot of cuckoos call us up and tell us wild stories. We have to check them out, because a person can be crazy but still know a little piece of the truth."

"Do you think it will be dangerous, Dad?"

Menetti sighed. "No. I don't. I think it will just be sad."

After a long hour that included a stop at Howard Johnson's for milk shakes, they reached Willimantic. Menetti gave his deputy his orders. "First, no one must know we're here or that we ever came here; and second, you must not talk to me while I try to find Baily Street, because being talked to while I'm getting lost in a strange city makes me very jumpy. Understood?"

The deputy nodded.

Willimantic is a small city east of Hartford. From the highway one can see a cluster of turn-of-the-century brick manufacturing buildings, like the abandoned textile mills of eastern Massachusetts. Once down into the warren of streets of the town, Menetti found his way to a grimy neighborhood of frame houses, the sort of neighborhood with a launderette on every second block and a tavern on every corner. On a street of sooty two-family houses he asked a man in khakis and a lumber jacket for Baily Street, and got a blank stare.

Menetti pushed on. After four or five blocks he stopped a woman coming in from her yard with a basket of wash. She was pretty sure Baily Street was somewhere on the north side.

As Menetti felt his way from one street to the next, a sad black ball of embarrassment began to grow inside him. This was a truly dumb thing to be doing. If the DA's office ever found out, if the press got one whiff of it . . . For that matter, if Eugene told Pat how they spent the day and she figured out what he'd been up to . . . Menetti glanced over at his deputy, who was sitting erect, studying the passing neighborhood, with his pistol at the ready. Well, he could do this much for Susan, keep the ripest nuts off her back. Afterward he and Eugene could have lunch; then the drive back would take two more hours, and by then they could go to a movie and kill the rest of the day. What do people do with kids all day?

He drove slowly through a small section of shops, and found his way into another residential neighborhood. Point Street. Canal Street. Baily Street. Well, I found it.

"Baily Street, sir!"

"Yes, I see, Deputy." Here they were. At least it wouldn't take long. He was glad he'd have Eugene for company on the way back. Then he wouldn't have to spend two hours driving alone with that sour restless feeling. Which way do the numbers go? Try on the right first.

The first numbers on the block were in the 3300s, and they were going down. He pulled into a driveway to turn around.

"Are we almost there, Dad?" Eugene whispered.

"Almost there, pal." He paused, peering to find a house number as he drove slowly down the street. Found one; 3812. Good. "Now, when we get there, Deputy, your job will be to guard the car. I won't be inside long, and I'll give you a full report when I'm done. You cover me from outside, okay?"

"Okay, sir. What number are we looking for, sir?"

"It's 4429. Sorry, Deputy. I should have told you sooner."

"Okay. We just passed 4018."

More dreary blocks to reach the 4400s. Okay, Malvina, thought Menetti. Here's your big chance to show me where Jesus sits and drinks tea with you; 4421, 4423, 4429. There you are, Malvina.

The car drifted to a stop. Menetti had switched off the ignition and turned to unlock his door before he saw it. Eugene watched his father freeze. The boy waited patiently, but nothing happened. Why wasn't his father getting out of the car? Eugene glanced up at him and was astonished to see that his eyes were glazed with tears. Eugene followed his father's gaze. He wasn't looking at 4429. He was looking at the house next door, a gray house with peeling paint and a torn screen on the door. In front of the house was parked an old blue car with rust spots all over the doors, and on the front-right wheel, a whitewall tire.

"Daddy?" whispered Eugene after a minute.

"Oh, my God," said his father. "Susan . . ." He put up both hands to cover his face, and for a second or two, he really cried.

MENETTI dried his eyes and nose with his big handkerchief. He told Eugene to stay in the car, head low, and watch the house next to 4429. If anyone came out, Eugene was to lean on the horn. "I'll be right back," he said.

Menetti walked up to 4429 and rang the bell. He was still not very far from tears. He hoped he'd have a grip on himself when he had to speak again.

The door was opened by a tiny black woman with cloud-white hair. She was wearing glasses and an apron, and she greeted Menetti with a look of annoyance. "Well, you certainly took your time, Lieutenant," she said with perfect mad confidence after he had introduced himself. "Come in here before he sees you." She tipped her head in the direction of the house next door.

Menetti stepped into her living room, which was dark and tidy. "Thank you," he said. "May I use your phone?"

"Right there," said Malvina, pointing. He dialed O and said to the operator, "Get me the police, please. This is an emergency."

Malvina was looking out the window. "I don't see no squad cars," she said suspiciously. "You don't have much time; he goes to work in the hospital afternoons, you know."

Menetti said into the phone, "This is Detective Albert Menetti, Boston PD. . . . Yes. I'm at 4429 Baily Street. It looks like a long shot just paid off for me here, but I'm without any backup. . . . Yes, a missing child. Alex Selky. I haven't actually seen him, but I'm pretty sure. Could I have two unmarked cars, please, as fast as you can. No sirens. I'll wait for you in my car across the street. A gray Plymouth."

Ten minutes later, while four policemen with drawn guns covered them from the street, Menetti stood with two plainclothes detectives on the porch of 4431. He rang the bell. Silence. An eternal wait. And then the door was opened by Alex Selky.

Menetti felt the breath lock in his lungs as it collided once again with a painful urge toward tears—this small, very thin boy with the perfect round head, and eyes that blinked in the bright winter sunlight. His hair was cut ragged and short, dyed a flat corn color. The nails on his small hands were gnawed to the quick. As he stood in the cold holding the door open, Menetti could see a lavender bruise on the inside of his left forearm.

A man came to the door behind Alex. He was dressed in a white polyester pantsuit and white canvas shoes, the uniform of a male nurse. He had a plump pink face, and one brown eye looked off to the right into space. In the living room behind him, Menetti could see the fluorescent blue flicker of the television.

"Yes?" said the man, putting a fleshy hand on Alex's head. "What is it?"

Menetti heard the echo of a thousand rehearsals of the words he had ceased to believe he would ever say. "You are under arrest for the kidnapping of Alexander Selky. You have the right to remain silent. . . ." The man never moved as he was given his rights. He just stared mildly at the men on his porch, as if he half wondered what had taken them so long.

When the handcuffs appeared, Alex, looking bewildered, shrank back and began to whimper, but the man with the walleye said only, "Allen, would you please turn off the TV?" And Alex immediately turned back into the living room to do so, and thus missed seeing the man with the walleye being taken away.

Menetti, fighting an urge to scoop the boy up and hold him, followed Alex inside. Alex whirled around when Menetti entered the room, and edged away from him. Menetti went into the kitchen, where, against a counter littered with open boxes of cereal, jars of jelly, and a container of milk, he found a phone and dialed Susan's number. It rang ten times. He hung up and asked an operator to dial it for him. Again, no answer. He went back out onto the porch, where the remaining policemen were waiting for him, openmouthed with excitement.

"Alex Selky! No kidding!" one of them said. "Didn't you arrest a guy for killing him?"

Menetti nodded. His throat ached with joy . . . rage. It had been all he could do, in the moment his gaze met the mild, skewed one in the plump, babyish face, to keep from lunging at the man and battering his head against the doorframe.

"Look," Menetti said now. "I can't reach the mother. What I want to do is just take this boy home the fastest way I can. Can I get an escort?"

"I'll call headquarters," said one of the officers. He went to his car and, leaning in the driver's side, made a call on the radio. He was back in a moment. "You got it," he said. "They just arrived with our man, and the place is going nuts."

"Okay, good," said Menetti. He went back in to Alex and knelt to talk to him eye to eye.

"Alex, my name is Detective Menetti, and I'm going to take you home to your mommy."

Alex just stared at him, his face blank and wary. Menetti held out his hand, and Alex looked at it, then drew back.

Menetti stood up. "Just come on now, Alex," he commanded, and he walked outside. Alex put on a cheap blue parka and followed him onto the porch.

"A team is on its way over to search the house," said one of the waiting policemen. "We can go as soon as they get here."

"Good," said Menetti. The policemen stared at Alex and smiled at him. Alex stared back at them. Menetti suddenly wondered if his pupils were unnaturally constricted. Drugged? His heart groaned. He thought of the nurse's uniform. That gutless creep. It must have been so easy for him.

ALEX stood on the porch, utterly alone. Walter was gone. He was supposed to keep the door locked all the time whenever Walter was gone. He knew what happened if Walter came home and found it open. What he didn't know was what happened if Walter didn't come home. He had wondered about that every time Walter locked him in and drove away. He had a pretty good idea that Walter wasn't coming back this time.

And now there was this one. My-name-is-Detective-Miniddy-I'm-going-to-take-you-to-your-mommy. Uh-huh. Walter wasn't a detective. Why should this one be? Walter hadn't taken him to his daddy. Why should this one take him to Mommy all of a sudden, after all this time? She changed her mind again?

Here comes another car up the street, and it stops at our house. Out get four more men. Here they all come up the steps. If they take me somewhere else, what will happen to my birds?

I hope where they take me next there's a TV. There was no TV in the last place.

This Detective Miniddy is squatting down again talking to me. Come, Alex. Well, he has a better car than ours. . . . Gee, he even already has a boy. Maybe this one will be with me at the next place. It would be good to have another kid.

Menetti, holding the front door of his car open, didn't know if he wanted to give all his attention to Alex or if he wanted to never have to look at that blank stare again in his life. He had an overwhelming desire to stop everything for a minute and sit down and pray.

Eugene was agog. "Dad . . ." he breathed. "We found Alex, didn't we? How did you know? Are we going to be famous?"

"Alex," said Menetti, "this is my son Eugene. Eugene, this is Alex. Do you want to ride up here with us, Alex?"

Alex said nothing. Eugene gestured excitedly for Alex to get in beside him. Alex climbed obediently into the car and sat down, facing straight ahead.

When Menetti pulled out into the street, one of the police cars fell in behind them. From the radio came crackling instructions. "Left at the second light. Okay, stay in the right lane."

"That's a police radio," Eugene whispered to Alex. Alex was studying it. He glanced up and eyed Eugene.

"Dad," said Eugene quickly, "could I show him how our microphone works?"

Menetti said, "Good idea. Tell our escort we read them."

Eugene knew how it was done. "We copy," he said sternly into the microphone. "Do you read me?"

"Loud and clear," said the following car. "Take your next right on Barrow Street. You'll pick up the signs for Route 6."

"Here, you do it."

Eugene handed Alex the mike, and after a moment Alex said into it, "We copy," and then handed it quickly back to Eugene.

"Ten four," said the car behind them.

When they reached the highway, Menetti clamped his foot down on the gas and picked up to eighty. The police car behind them stayed on their tail, and Menetti knew the police would be alerting Connecticut Highway Patrol of their approach.

"Unmarked gray Plymouth with police escort proceeding east on Route 6, on urgent police business. . . . Yeah, that's right. We found the Selky kid. . . . Yes, alive. . . . No, thank you, no assistance needed. Just keep the lanes clear and pass the word."

Eugene nudged Alex and pointed to the speedometer. The needle quivered above eighty. Alex looked at it, then back at Eugene. They both looked up at Menetti.

"Are we going to go this fast all the way to Boston, Dad?" asked Eugene.

"Yes, unless it scares you."

"No way!" cried Eugene.

"Are we going too fast for you, Alex?" Alex shook his head.

"Does his mom know we're coming, Dad?" asked Eugene.

"No, she doesn't. I tried to call her, but she must be out."

"She's always out," said Alex suddenly.

"What do you mean?" Menetti turned to him, but Alex had clamped his lips shut.

"Boy, is your mom going to be excited," Eugene whispered to Alex. Alex glanced over, a look that said that Eugene knew nothing about other people's family affairs.

"I've seen your mom on television about fifty times, telling everyone to keep looking for you. And my dad's been looking for you for almost a year. Didn't you see it on the news?"

Alex shook his head.

"They had these posters with pictures of you all over the place. Didn't you see those?" Eugene went on. "And my dad was in charge of looking for you. Weren't you, Dad?"

"Yes," said Menetti softly. "I was."

Alex looked from one to the other. He wasn't surprised. Walter had told him the police would be looking for him.

Their car sped through the countryside. "Hey," Eugene whispered after a while. He guessed that his father had some reason for not asking Alex questions, but Eugene couldn't contain himself. "Did he keep you tied up?"

"What?"

"The guy who kidnapped you."

Menetti gave no sign that he was listening. The two small bodies on the passenger side seemed to him to take less room on the seat than one full-size adult. He had always marveled at how kids could slip into a child world where they seemed to assume that the adult driving the car had been struck deaf.

Alex looked perturbed. "My daddy hired Walter to pick me up. It was a secret from Mommy. She wanted me to go to school instead of seeing Daddy."

"You mean you were with your daddy all that time?"

"No," said Alex impatiently. "We went to this room and waited for a few days, but Daddy never came. He forgot."

Eugene was horrified. "I bet you cried a lot."

"I did." Alex's impassivity slipped a little. For a moment his face was congested with the memory of those first days.

"Well, then, why didn't you go back home?"

"Mommy told Walter not to bother. She was mad at me for going with Walter, and she couldn't afford me anymore anyway because I eat a lot. Walter called her around Christmas because I thought she might want me for Christmas, but she told him that was all right, she got another little boy now."

Menetti couldn't keep silent for more of this. "Alex, he just told you those things. They're not true. Your father didn't hire him, and your mother has been looking for you every minute since you disappeared. She missed you very much and she never gave up wanting you back."

Alex studied him with a face that was shrewd and thoughtful. He said nothing.

They sped to the end of the Massachusetts Turnpike, then went north to the Mass Pike Extension and started into Boston. There, city traffic hemmed them in, and the police car behind them had trouble staying with them.

"Will his mommy be there when we get to his house?"

"I don't know, Eugene. They've probably found her by now." Alex was perched forward on the seat, studying the passing city sights, deep in concentration. "Is it getting familiar, Alex?" Menetti asked.

No answer.

They reached the Copley Square exit, where the Willimantic police car caught up with them at the traffic light. Together the two cars drove across Dartmouth Street. Alex was watchful and silent, Eugene was beginning to tense with excitement, and Menetti was numb, wondering what he was heading for.

"She's going to be so *excited*," Eugene whispered to Alex with dramatic earnestness. "She's gonna be *so* excited. We're almost there, Dad, right? Aren't we almost there?"

Alex's gaze flicked warily from one of them to the other. It *was* his neighborhood. Maybe they could be taking him to his mommy. But probably they were taking him to jail.

They stopped at the corner of Marlborough. Alex could almost see Justine's house from here. He sat up straighter and craned his neck, as if he might see someone he knew. What an odd feeling. The feeling of something familiar. He let something flicker inside him, like the shadow of a high-flying bird flashing across a patch of sunlight. Was it possible that he could be allowed to go home?

"Look," yelled Eugene, "there's a poster of you, Alex! See it?" Alex looked, and there in the window of a secretarial school was a poster. STILL MISSING. And under the words, the smiling face. Alex looked at it. Missing. They were missing him? He almost let himself smile, but then he caught on to the trick. Missing. Wanted. He'd seen Wanted posters of other bad people in a post office once. Walter pointed them out. "And they know all about you, too," Walter had said. So Alex never made a peep when he went anywhere with Walter. He kept his head down.

Menetti stepped on the gas hard. He wanted to get to Susan. Behind him the Willimantic police car turned on its siren. The sudden urgent howl of it seemed to echo and reecho from the walls, a sound that filled Alex with cold certainty.

SUSAN had taken Taxi with her to lunch in the South End with two of her Harvard colleagues, and afterward she walked him the long way home. She was just coming up Marlborough Street when she heard the siren. Pushing her hands deep into her pockets and breathing a cloud into the bitter February air, she thought, Another accident or another crime. Ah, poor souls.

It was only when the noise kept growing louder and louder, as if it were coming for her, that she began to feel afraid. It was more instinctive than specific. She was here, Taxi was here, they'd never again bring Graham home to her. What else did she have to lose?

The siren died as she turned the corner into Fremont Street. She saw so many cars and trucks and people crowded into the street that her heart lurched. She felt herself go cold with dread and forced herself to keep walking.

There were so many people milling up and down her steps, pointing to her, pointing to the street, pointing to each other, that she didn't know where to look first. There were police and news vans, but no fire trucks that she could see. Surprise and fear seemed to freeze the scene before her, so she took it in slow motion. It seemed to be happening in a silent bubble world out of time and feeling. There was a car pulling up that looked just like Menetti's. The two front doors of the car opened at the same time, and Menetti emerged from the driver's side and stood there in the street looking at her, an intense, beseeching look, as if he were trying to say something to her but couldn't open his mouth. His presence made no sense to her at all.

As he scurried through the crowd to the sidewalk, she saw that he had some of his kids with him. The shorter one was probably Eugene, but the other kid, in a blue parka, looked a little older. Judging every small boy as she always did, she dismissed this one as taller than Alex, with dull, short dun-colored hair. She moved forward. Now she knew: her father was dead. No, she'd left the iron on; the house was burning. . . . Margaret. Margaret was hurt, or trapped. . . .

It wasn't until Taxi bolted away from her down the sidewalk, barking with lunatic joy, that she stopped cold and looked at the two children again. Taxi leaped at the blue parka. She looked again and this time really saw the face.

He was there, a dozen paces away from her. Right there. Her brain seemed to disconnect from her vision, as if she could see, but not understand what she saw.

Menetti was with the boys now, and she looked at him with mildness and wonder. It was all so incredibly strange. She was a lake of puzzled feeling dammed up behind the thinnest membrane. How could this be so confusing? How could there be so much to absorb? This was the simplest moment of her life.

It all broke open inside her as she looked back to Alex and just opened her arms to him, and in that moment got past the Alex of the missing months to her own boy. She saw him smile. And then he cried, "Mommy!" And she was on her knees on the frozen sidewalk blind with tears when her son flung himself into her arms.

On Meeting Beth Gutcheon . . .

Beth Gutcheon

It comes as a delightful surprise to see that the creator of a novel as emotionally wrenching as *Still Missing* is a fresh-faced young woman who thoroughly enjoys the varied aspects of her busy life. In conversation she is warmly responsive, her remarks are tempered by humor and a keen intelligence, and she seems not at all impressed with herself, although at thirty-six she has achieved great success in two areas of creativity. In addition to being an accomplished novelist, Beth Gutcheon is an expert quilt maker and author of *The Perfect Patchwork Primer*.

It is impossible to read *Still Missing* without wondering whether Beth Gutcheon has had some close association with a kidnapping. She has not. Her interest in the subject stems from the fact that she learned firsthand what loving a child could mean. She is one of six children in a close and loving family, and her mother never fully recovered from the loss of a six-year-old daughter who died in the course of a routine tonsillectomy.

When asked about the aftereffects of an experience like Alex Selky's, Beth replied that she feels a child from a loving home would probably recover in time. She points out that children often perceive events quite differently from adults, so an episode that might seem permanently scarring to an adult could in fact be recalled by a child as merely unpleasant. If an adult can keep from displaying his own shock and horror, a child's innocence might keep him from having those feelings.

Beth grew up in Sewickley, Pennsylvania, and graduated from Radcliffe College. She lives with her architect husband, Jeffrey, and their eleven-year-old son in a Manhattan loft that Jeffrey has skillfully adapted into living quarters. Beth's next book should be a distinct change of pace, for it is a children's fantasy entitled *The Voyages of Edgar Rice Pudding*.

All Things Bright and Beautiful,
All Creatures Great and Small,
All Things Wise and Wonderful…

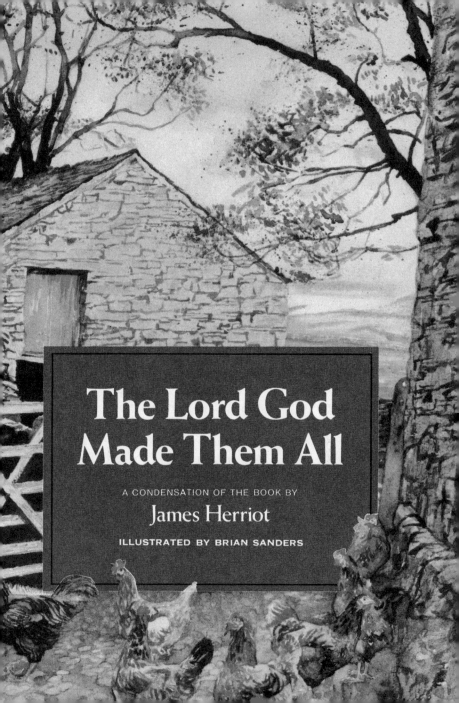

The Lord God Made Them All

A CONDENSATION OF THE BOOK BY

James Herriot

ILLUSTRATED BY BRIAN SANDERS

After a stint in the RAF, James Herriot—
that engaging veterinary surgeon from the
Yorkshire Dales—is home at last. But
in the aftermath of World War II, the spirit
of change is in the wind. New drugs are
revolutionizing animal medicine. And in
the Herriot household there is now a
roguish young son, Jimmy.

Whether our vet is treating an ailing cow,
making a midnight call on a hypochondriacal
dog owner, or nervously awaiting the birth
of his second child, he never loses the wry
humor or the rare sense of joy that have
made his *All Creatures Great and Small* and
All Things Bright and Beautiful favorites
the world over.

1

THE high moorland road was unfenced, and my car wheels ran easily from the strip of tarmac onto the turf, cropped to a velvet closeness by the sheep. I stopped the engine, got out and looked around me.

The road cut cleanly through the grass and heather before dipping into the valley beyond. This was one of the good places where I could see into two dales. The whole land was spread beneath me: the soft fields in the valley floors, the grazing cattle, the rivers edged with pebbles in places, thickly fringed with trees in others. The brilliant green of the walled pastures pushed up the sides of the fells until the heather and the harsh moor grass began, and only the walls were left, climbing to the mottled summits, disappearing over the bare ridges that marked the beginning of the wild country.

I leaned against the car, and the wind blew the cold sweet air around me. I had been back in civilian life only a few weeks, after a spell in the Royal Air Force. During that spell I had thought constantly of Yorkshire, but I had forgotten how beautiful it was. Just thinking from afar could not evoke the peace, the solitude, the sense of the nearness of the wild that make the Dales both thrilling and comforting. Among the crowds of men and the stale air of the towns it had been hard to conjure up a place where I could be quite alone on the wide green roof of England, where every breath was filled with the scent of grass.

I had had a disturbing morning. Everywhere I had gone I was reminded that I had come back to a world of change, and I did not like change. One old farmer saying, "It's all t'needle now, Mr. Herriot," as I injected his cow, had made me look down at the syringe in my hand and realize suddenly that this was what I was doing most of the time these days.

I knew what he meant. Only a few years before, I would more likely have "drenched" his cow—grabbed it by the nose and poured a pint of medicine down its throat. We still carried a special drenching bottle around with us—an empty wine bottle with no shoulders, which allowed the liquid to run easily. Often we would mix the medicine with black treacle from the barrel that stood in the corner of most cow byres. But all this was disappearing, and the farmer's remark brought it home to me that things were never going to be the same again.

Now, after the war, a revolution was beginning in agriculture and in veterinary practice. Farming was becoming more scientific, and concepts cherished for generations were being abandoned, while in the veterinary world new surgical procedures and drugs such as sulfa and penicillin were slowly sweeping our old treatments into oblivion. There were signs, too, that the small farmers were on the way out. These men, some with only six cows, a few pigs and poultry, still made up most of our practice, but they were beginning to wonder if they could make a living on this scale, and one or two had already sold out to the bigger men. The small farmers—old men doggedly doing what they have always done for the sole reason that they have always done it—were the men I cherished, the truly rich characters living by the ancient values, speaking the old Yorkshire dialect that television and radio have almost swamped.

I took a last long breath and got into my car. As I looked out at the great fells thrusting their bald summits into the clouds, tier upon tier of them, timeless, indestructible, towering over the glories beneath, I felt better immediately. The Dales had not changed at all.

I did one more call, then drove back to our office, the spacious, elegant Skeldale House. The place looked much the same as when I had first seen it years ago, but it had seen change, too. My partner, Siegfried Farnon, had married, as had his younger brother, Tristan. They had both moved out, but Siegfried was living only a few miles outside our town of Darrowby. My wife, Helen, and I and our little son, Jimmy, now had the run of the whole house. Tristan, alas, had left our practice. When the war ended, he was Captain Farnon of the Royal Army veterinary corps, and he went on to join the Ministry of Agriculture as an infertility investigation officer. He left a sad gap in our lives, but fortunately we still saw him and his wife regularly.

I opened the front door, and halfway to the dispensary I almost bumped into Siegfried. He was storming along the passage, and he grabbed my arm in an agitated manner. "Ah, James, just the man I was looking for! I've had the most ghastly time this morning. I knocked the exhaust pipe off my car going up that bloody awful track to High Liston, and now I'm without transport until the repair can be done. It's maddening!"

"That's all right, Siegfried. I'll do your calls."

"No, no, James, it's kind of you, but don't you see, this sort of thing is going to happen again and again. That's what I want to talk to you about. We need a spare car."

"A spare?"

"That's right. Something to fall back upon at a time like this. As a matter of fact, I rang Hammond at the garage to bring round something suitable for us to look at. I think I hear him outside now."

My partner was always one for instant action, and I followed him out the front door. Mr. Hammond was there with a 1933 Morris Oxford, and Siegfried trotted down the steps toward it.

"A hundred pounds, you said, eh, Mr. Hammond?" He walked around the car, picking pieces of rust from the black paintwork and peering at the upholstery. "Ah well, it's seen better days, but the appearance doesn't matter as long as it goes all right."

"It's a sound little job, Mr. Farnon," the garage proprietor said. "New battery, and a good bit o' tread on the tires."

"Mmmm." Siegfried shook the rear bumper with his foot, and the old springs groaned. "How about the brakes? Important in this hilly country."

"They're champion, Mr. Farnon. First-rate."

My colleague nodded slowly. "Good, good. You don't mind if I drive her round the block?"

"Nay, nay, of course not," Mr. Hammond replied. "Give 'er any trial you like." He was a man who prided himself on his imperturbability, and he dropped confidently into the passenger seat as Siegfried took the wheel.

"Hop in, James!" my partner cried. I opened the rear door and took my place behind Mr. Hammond.

Siegfried took off abruptly with a roaring and creaking from the old vehicle, and despite the garage man's outward calm, his shirt collar rose a couple of inches above his jacket as we shot along Trengate Street. The collar subsided a little when Siegfried slowed down to turn left, but reappeared spasmodically as we negotiated a series of sharp and narrow bends at top speed.

When we reached a long, straight lane that runs parallel to Trengate, Siegfried thundered along it. At the end of the lane he came almost to a halt as he turned left again. "I think we'll test the brakes, Mr. Hammond," he said, and suddenly hurled the car ahead. He really meant to carry out a thorough test! The roar of the ancient engine rose to a scream and the Trengate crossing approached with frightening rapidity. When Siegfried braked, the car slued violently to the right, and as we catapulted crabwise into Trengate, Mr. Hammond's head was jammed against the roof and his entire shirt back was exposed. When we came to a halt, he slid slowly back into his seat. At no time had he spoken or, apart from his movements, shown any emotion.

At our front door we got out, and my colleague rubbed his chin doubtfully. "She does pull a little to the right on braking, Mr. Hammond. Perhaps you have another vehicle available?"

The garage man did not answer for a few moments. His spectacles were askew and he was very pale. "Aye . . . aye . . ." he said shakily. "I 'ave another little job might suit you."

"Capital!" Siegfried rubbed his hands. "Perhaps you could

bring it along after lunch, and we can have a spin round to try it."

Mr. Hammond's eyes widened and he swallowed a few times. "I'm goin' to be busy this afternoon, Mr. Farnon. I'll send one of me men."

We bade him good-by, and as we went back into the house my partner put an arm across my shoulders. "Well, James, another step toward increasing the efficiency of the practice. Anyway"—he smiled—"I rather enjoy these little interludes."

Suddenly I began to feel good. So many things were new and different, but the Dales hadn't changed, and Siegfried hadn't changed either.

2

"Hello! Hello!" I bellowed.

"Hello! Hello!" little Jimmy piped just behind me.

I turned and looked at my son. He was four years old now and had been coming on my rounds with me for over a year. Clearly he considered himself a veteran of the farmyards.

This shouting was a common habit of mine. When a vet arrived on a farm, it was often surprisingly difficult to find the farmer. He might be on a tractor half a mile across the fields, or in one of the barns, so I always relied on a few brisk shouts to locate him. Jimmy had caught on to the practice, and there was no doubt he enjoyed the opportunity to exercise his lungs. I watched him as he strutted importantly over the cobbles, giving tongue every few seconds. He was also making an unnecessary amount of noise by clattering on the rough stones with his new boots.

Those boots were his pride, the final recognition of his status as veterinary assistant. When I first began to take him around with me, his reaction was the simple joy of a child at being able to see animals of all kinds, particularly the young ones, and the thrill of discovery when he came upon a huddle of kittens in the straw or found a bitch with pups in a box stall. Before long, however, he wanted to get into the action. The contents of my car trunk were soon as familiar to him as his toy box at home, and he delighted in handing out the tins of stomach powder, the white lotion and the long cartons of Universal Cattle Medicine. Finally he began to forestall me by rushing back to the car for the calcium and the flutter valve as soon as he saw a recumbent cow. He had become a diagnostician as well.

I think the thing he enjoyed most was accompanying me on an evening call, if Helen would allow him to postpone his bedtime. He was in heaven driving into the country in the darkness, training my flashlight on a cow's teat while I stitched it.

The farmers were always kind to him. Even the most uncommunicative would grunt, "Ah see you've got t'apprentice with ye," as we got out of the car.

Those farmers had something Jimmy coveted: their big hobnailed boots. He had a great admiration for farmers in general, strong hardy men who spent their lives in the open and who pushed fearlessly among plunging packs of cattle and slapped the rumps of massive cart horses. I could see he was deeply impressed as he watched them mounting granary steps carrying sacks weighing two hundred pounds on their shoulders, or hanging on casually to the noses of huge bullocks, their boots slithering over the floor.

It was those boots that got under Jimmy's skin most of all. Sturdy and unyielding, they seemed to symbolize for him the character of the men who wore them.

Matters came to a head one day when we were conversing in the car. Or rather, my son was doing the conversing in the form of a barrage of questions, which went on pretty well nonstop every day and followed a well-tried formula. "What is the fastest train—the *Blue Peter* or the *Flying Scotsman?*"

"Well . . . I should say the *Blue Peter.*"

Then, getting into deeper water, "Is a giant train faster than a phantom racing car?"

"That's a difficult one. Maybe the phantom racer is faster."

Jimmy changed his tack suddenly. "That was a big man at the last farm, wasn't he?"

"He certainly was."

"Was he bigger than Mr. Robinson?"

We were launching into his favorite game—"big man"—and I

knew how it would end, but I played my part. "Oh yes, he was."

"Was he bigger than Mr. Kirkley?"

"Without a doubt."

Jimmy gave me a sidelong glance, and I knew he was about to play his two trump cards. "Was he bigger than the gas man?"

The towering gentleman who came to read the gas meters at Skeldale House had always fascinated my son, and I had to reply very carefully. "Well, you know, I really think he was."

"Ah, but . . ." The corner of Jimmy's mouth twitched up craftily. "Was he bigger than Mr. Thackray?"

That was the killer punch. Nobody was bigger than Mr. Thackray, who looked down on the other inhabitants of Darrowby from six feet seven inches.

I shrugged my shoulders in defeat. "No, I have to admit it. He wasn't as big as Mr. Thackray."

Jimmy smiled and nodded, well satisfied. This put him in such high good humor that he broached something that must have been on his mind for some time.

"Daddy," he said. "Can I have some boots?"

"Boots? But you've got some already." I pointed down at the little Wellingtons in which Helen always rigged him before he set out for the farms.

He gazed at his feet sadly before replying. "Yes, I know, but I want proper boots like the farmers."

This was a facer. I didn't know what to say. "But, Jim, little boys don't have boots like that. Maybe when you're bigger . . ."

"Oh, I want them now," he moaned in anguished tones.

At first I thought it was a passing whim, but he kept up his campaign, reinforcing it with disgusted looks as Helen drew on the Wellingtons each morning. His listless slouch conveyed the message that his footwear was entirely unsuitable for a man like him. Finally Helen and I talked it over one night after he had gone to bed.

"They surely don't have farm boots his size, do they?" I asked.

Helen shook her head. "I wouldn't have thought so, but I'll look around, in any case."

And within a week my wife returned from shopping flushed

with success and bearing the smallest pair of farm boots I had ever seen. I couldn't help laughing. They were so tiny, yet so perfect—thick hobnailed soles, chunky uppers and a long row of lace holes with metal loops at the top.

Jimmy didn't laugh when he saw them. He handled them almost with awe, and once he had got them on, his demeanor changed. He was naturally square-set and jaunty, but to see him striding around a farmyard in those boots you would think he owned the place. He clumped and stamped, held himself very upright, and his cries of "Hello! Hello!" took on a new authority.

He was never what I would call naughty, but he had that bit of devil which I suppose all boys need to have. He liked to assert himself, and he was not above taking advantage of me in awkward situations. There was one afternoon when Mr. Garrett brought in his sheep dog. The animal was very lame, and as I hoisted him onto the consulting-room table, a small head appeared outside the window that overlooked the sunlit garden.

I didn't mind that. Jimmy often watched me treat our patients, and I half expected him to come in for a closer look.

It is often difficult to locate the source of a dog's lameness, but in this case I found it immediately. When I gently squeezed the outside pad on one foot he winced, and a tiny bead of serum appeared on the black surface. "Something's in there, Mr. Garrett," I said. "Probably a thorn. I'll have to give him a local anesthetic and open it up."

It was when I was filling the syringe that a knee came into view outside, at the corner of the window. Jimmy surely couldn't be climbing the wisteria! It was dangerous, and I had expressly forbidden it. The branches of the beautiful creeper curled all over the back of the house, and though they were as thick as a man's leg near ground level, they became quite slender as they made their way up to the roof. No, I decided that I'd been mistaken, and I injected the quick-acting anesthetic. I reached for the scalpel. "Hold his leg up and keep it steady," I said.

Serious-faced and obviously deeply concerned about his dog, Mr. Garrett nodded, and pursed his lips in apprehension as I poised my knife.

For me it was an absorbing moment. With the point of my blade I made a careful nick in the pad, and at that moment a shadow crossed the window. I glanced up. It was Jimmy. The little blighter *was* on the wisteria, but there was nothing I could do about it then except to give him a quick glare.

I cut a little deeper and squeezed, but still nothing showed in the wound. I didn't want to make a big hole, but it was clear that I would need a cross-shaped incision to see farther down. I was drawing the scalpel at right angles to my first cut when, from the corner of my eye, I spotted two feet dangling just below the top of the window. I tried to concentrate on my job, but the feet swung and kicked repeatedly, obviously for my benefit. At last they disappeared, which could only mean that their owner was ascending to the dangerous regions.

I dug down a little deeper and swabbed with cotton wool. Ah yes, I could see something now. I reached for forceps, and just then Jimmy's head showed itself again, upside down this time. He was hanging by his feet from the branches, and the face was positively leering. In deference to my client I had been trying to ignore the byplay from outside, but this was too much. I leaped at the glass and shook my fist violently. My fury must have startled the performer, because the face vanished instantly and I could hear faint sounds of feet scrambling upward. That was not much comfort; however, I forced myself back to my task.

"Sorry, Mr. Garrett," I said. "Will you hold the leg up again, please?"

He complied with a thin smile, and I pushed my forceps into the depths. They grated on something hard. I gripped, pulled gently and—oh, lovely—out came the pointed, glistening head of a thorn. It was one of the tiny triumphs that lighten vets' lives. I was beaming at my client and patting his dog when I heard a crack, followed by a howl of terror. Then a small form hurtled past the window and thudded with horrid force into the garden.

I shot outside. Jimmy was already sitting up among the wallflowers, and I was too relieved to be angry.

"Have you hurt yourself?" I gasped, and he shook his head.

I lifted him to his feet and felt him over carefully. There appeared to be no damage. "Go along and see Mummy," I said, and returned to the consulting room.

"Is he all right?" Mr. Garrett asked.

"Yes, I think so. But I do apologize for rushing out. . . ."

Mr. Garrett laid his hand on my shoulder. "Say no more, Mr. Herriot. I have children of my own." And then he spoke the words that have become engraved on my heart. "You need nerves of steel to be a parent."

Later at tea I watched my son slap plum jam on a slice of bread. Thank heaven he was no worse for his fall, but still I had to remonstrate with him. "Young man," I said, "that was a very naughty thing you did out there. I've told you again and again not to climb the wisteria."

Jimmy bit into his bread and jam and regarded me impassively. I could see that he wasn't taking what I was saying too seriously.

"If you're going to behave like this," I went on, "I'm not going to take you round the farms with me. I'll just have to find another little boy to help me with my cases."

I looked for some reaction in this morsel of humanity who was much later to become a far better veterinary surgeon than I could ever be. "Another little boy?" Jimmy inquired.

"That's right. I can't have naughty boys with me. I'll have to find somebody else."

Jimmy thought this over for a minute or so and appeared to accept the situation philosophically.

Then in a flash his sangfroid evaporated. He looked up at me in wide-eyed alarm and his voice came out in a high quaver. "Would he have my boots?"

3

"It was Hemingway who said that, wasn't it?"

Norman Beaumont shook his head. "No, Scott Fitzgerald."

I didn't argue, because Norman usually knew. In fact, it was one of the attractive things about him.

I enjoyed having veterinary students see practice with us. They helped with fetching and carrying, opened gates, and were company on our lonely rounds. In return they absorbed priceless experience from us in the practical side of their education.

Since the war, however, I found I was learning almost as much from these young men as they were learning from me, because veterinary teaching had taken such a leap forward. The vast new field of small-animal work was opening up dramatically. Advanced surgical procedures were being carried out on farm animals, too, and today's students had the great advantage of being able to see such things done in schools equipped with modern operating theaters.

Norman Beaumont was in his final year and was a deep well of information, at which I drank greedily. But apart from the veterinary side we had a common love of reading. When we weren't talking shop, the conversation was usually on literary lines, and Norman's companionship made the journeys between farms seem short.

He was immensely likable, with a personality that was formal and dignified beyond his twenty-two years and was only just saved from pomposity by a gentle humor. A solid citizen in the making if ever I saw one, and this impression was strengthened by his slightly pear-shaped physique and the fact that he was determinedly trying to cultivate a pipe.

As we drove along, I got onto the topic of the new operations. "And you say they are actually doing cesareans on cows in the college clinics?"

Norman applied a match to his pipe. "Doing them like hotcakes; it's a regular thing." His words would have carried more weight if he had been able to blow a puff of smoke out after them, but he had filled the bowl too tightly, and despite a fierce sucking that hollowed his cheeks and ballooned his eyeballs, he couldn't manage a draw.

"Gosh, you don't know how lucky you are," I said. "The hours I've slaved on byre floors calving cows, knocking my guts out trying to bring heads round or reach feet. And if only I'd known how, I could have saved myself the trouble with a nice straightforward operation. What sort of a job is it, anyway?"

The student gave me a superior smile. "Nothing much to it,

really." He relit his pipe, tamped the tobacco down and winced as he burned his finger. "Takes about an hour, and no hard labor."

"Sounds marvelous," I said wistfully. "It's so much easier to tackle these jobs when you've seen a lot of them done."

"True, true." The student spread his hands. "But of course, most bovine parturitions don't need a cesarean, and I'm always glad to have a calving for my casebook."

I nodded in agreement. Norman's casebook was a heavily bound volume with every scrap of interesting material meticulously entered under headings in red ink. The examiners always wanted to see these books, and this one would be worth a few extra marks to Norman in his finals.

I dropped the student at his digs in late afternoon and went back to Skeldale House for tea. I had just finished when Helen got up to answer the phone. "It's Mr. Bushell of Sycamore House," she told me. "He has a cow calving."

"Oh damn. I thought we'd have the evening to ourselves," I said as I put my cup down. "Tell him I'll be right out, Helen, will you?" I smiled as she put down the receiver. "One thing, Norman will be pleased. He was just saying he always welcomes a calving for his casebook."

I was right. The young man was in excellent humor when I called for him to drive out to the farm.

"I was reading some poetry when you rang the bell," he said. "You can always find something in poetry to apply to your life. How about now, when I'm expecting something interesting— *Hope springs eternal in the human breast.*"

"Alexander Pope's 'Essay on Man,'" I grunted. I wasn't feeling as enthusiastic as Norman. You never knew what was ahead on these occasions.

We drove through the farm gateway into the yard. The farmer led us into the byre, and in a stall opposite the window a small cow looked up at us anxiously from her straw bed. Above her head, her name, Bella, was chalked on a board.

"She isn't very big, Mr. Bushell," I shouted, remembering that he was hard of hearing.

"Aye, she allus was a poor doer. Had a rough time with her first calvin', but she milked well enough after it."

I observed the cow as I stripped off my shirt and soaped my arms. I didn't like the look of that narrow pelvis, and I breathed a silent prayer that there might be a tiny calf inside.

The farmer poked at the rump with his foot and shouted at the animal to make her rise. "She won't budge, Mr. Herriot," he said. "She's been painin' all day."

I didn't like the sound of that either. There was always something wrong when a cow strained so long without result. And the little animal did look utterly spent. Her head hung down and her eyelids drooped wearily.

Ah well, if she wouldn't get up, I had to get down. With my bare chest in contact with the ground, the thought occurred that cobbles didn't get any softer with the passage of the years. But when I slid my hand into the pelvic opening, I forgot my discomfort; it was villainously narrow. And beyond was something that froze my blood: two enormous hoofs, and a huge expanse of muzzle with twitching nostrils. As I withdrew my hand, the rough surface of the calf's tongue flicked briefly against my palm.

I sat back on my heels and raised my voice. "There's an elephant in there, Mr. Bushell. A tremendous calf, and no room for it to come out."

"Can't ye cut it away?"

"Afraid not. The calf's alive."

"Well, that's a beggar," Mr. Bushell said. "She's a good little milker. Ah don't want to send 'er to the butcher."

Neither did I. I hated the very thought of it. Then in a great moment of decision I turned to the student. "This is it, Norman! The ideal indication for a cesarean. What a good job you're with me!" I was slightly breathless with excitement, and I hardly noticed the flicker of anxiety in the young man's eyes.

I got to my feet and seized the farmer's arm. "Mr. Bushell, I'd like to do a cesarean operation on your cow—open her up and remove the calf surgically."

"Like they do sometimes wi' women?"

"That's right."

"Well that's a rum un." The farmer's eyebrows went up. "I never knew you could do that wi' cows."

"Oh, we can now," I said airily. "Things have moved on a bit in the last few years."

He rubbed a hand slowly across his mouth. "Well, ah don't know. I reckon she could die if you made a bloody great 'ole in her like that. Maybe she'd be better goin' for slaughter. I'd get a few quid for her."

I could see my big moment slipping away from me. "But she's only a thin little thing. She wouldn't be worth much for meat, and with a bit of luck we might get a live calf out of her."

I was going against one of my steadfast rules—never to talk a farmer into doing something—but I was seized by a kind of madness. Mr. Bushell looked at me for a long time; then, without changing expression, he nodded. "Awright, what do you need?"

"Two buckets of warm water, soap, towels," I replied. "And I'll bring some instruments into the house to boil, if I may."

When the farmer had departed, I thumped Norman on the shoulder. "This is just right. Plenty of light, a live calf to aim for, and as Mr. Bushell doesn't hear too well, I'll be able to ask you things as we go along."

Norman didn't say anything. I had him set up our equipment and scatter loose straw around the cow while I boiled the instruments in the farm kitchen. Soon syringes, suture materials, scalpels, scissors, local anesthetic and cotton wool were laid in a row on a clean towel draped over one of the bales. I added some antiseptic to the water and addressed the farmer. "We'll roll her over and you can hold the head down, Mr. Bushell."

Norman and I pushed at Bella's shoulder, and she flopped onto her side without resistance. I nudged the student. "Where do I make the incision?" I whispered.

Norman cleared his throat. "Well, er, it's about . . . ." He pointed.

I nodded. "Around the rumenotomy site, eh? But a bit lower, I suppose." I clipped away the hair from a foot-long strip. It would need a big opening for that calf to come through. Then I infiltrated the area with local anesthetic and began to cut. Under the peritoneum I was confronted with a protruding pink and white mass of tissue. I poked at it. There was something hard inside. Could it be the calf?

"Is that the rumen or the uterus?" I hissed. "It's pretty low down for the stomach, so I'd suppose it would be the uterus."

"Yes, that's the uterus all right."

"Good." I smiled in relief and made a bold incision. A great gout of impacted grass welled out, followed by a burst of gas and an outflow of dirty brown fluid.

I gasped. "It's the rumen. Look at all that mess!" I groaned as the filthy tide surged from the cow's first stomach into the abdominal cavity. "What the hell are you playing at, Norman?" He was trembling. "Thread me a needle. Quick!"

Norman shakily passed me a length of catgut. Wordlessly, dry-mouthed, I stitched up the gash I had made in the wrong organ. Then the two of us swabbed frantically at the escaped rumenal contents with cotton wool and antiseptic, but much of it had run away beyond our reach. The contamination must be massive.

When we had done what we could, I growled at the student, "I thought you knew all about these operations."

He looked frightened. "They do quite a few of them . . ."

I glared at him. "How many cesareans have you seen?"

"Well . . . er . . . one, actually."

"One! I thought you were an expert! Anyway, even if you'd seen only one, you should know a little bit about it."

"The thing is . . . I was right at the back of the class."

I worked up a sarcastic snarl. "Oh, I understand. So you couldn't see very well?"

"That's about it." The young man hung his head.

"Well, you're a stupid young fool!" I said in a vicious whisper. "Dishing out your confident instructions! You realize you've killed this good cow. With all that contamination she'll certainly develop peritonitis and die. All we can hope for now is to get the calf out alive." With an effort I turned my gaze from his stricken face. "Anyway, let's get on with it."

Apart from my first shout of panic, the entire interchange had been carried out pianissimo, and Mr. Bushell kept shooting inquiring glances at us. I gave him what I hoped was a reassuring smile and returned to the attack. Plunging my arm deep below what I now knew was the rumen, I encountered a smooth and mighty organ containing an enormous bulk with the hardness and immobility of a sack of coal. I felt my way along the surface and came upon the unmistakable contours of a hock pushing against the slippery wall. That was the calf, all right, but it was far, far away.

I withdrew my arm and started on Norman again. "From your position at the back of the class," I inquired bitingly, "did you happen to notice what they did next?"

"Next? Ah yes." He licked his lips. "You are supposed to exteriorize the uterus—bring it up to the wound."

I groaned. "King Kong couldn't lift that uterus! Have a feel."

The student, who was stripped and soaped like myself, introduced his arm for a moment. Then he withdrew it and nodded sheepishly. "You're right. It won't move."

"Only one thing to do. I'll have to cut into the uterus and grab that hock. There's nothing else to get hold of."

It was very nasty, fiddling about in the dark unknown, my arm buried to the shoulder in the cow, my tongue hanging out in anxiety. I was terrified I might slash into something vital, but in fact, it was my own fingers that I cut, several times, before I was able to draw the scalpel across the bulge made by the hock. A second later I had my hand around the hairy leg. Now I was getting somewhere.

Gingerly I enlarged the incision, inch by inch. I hoped fervently I had made it big enough as I seized the leg and tried to lift it. Immediately I knew that it was going to take tremendous strength to bring the calf into the light of day. Nowadays when I do a cesarean, I take care to have a big strong farm lad ready to help me, but that day I had only Norman.

"Come on," I panted. "Give me a hand."

We reached down together and began to pull. Teeth clenched, grunting with effort, we hauled upward till at last I was able to grasp the other hind leg. Even then, with a foot apiece in our hands, nothing wanted to move. As we lay back, pulling with every vestige of our strength, I had the sudden wave of illumination that comes to all members of our profession at times. I wished with all my heart I had never started this ghastly job.

But the calf was gradually coming through. The tail appeared, then an unbelievably massive rib cage and finally, with a rush, the shoulders and head. Norman and I sat down with a bump, the calf rolling over our knees, snorting and shaking his head.

"By gaw, he's a big un!" exclaimed the farmer.

I nodded. "Yes. One of the biggest I've ever seen. He'd never have come out the proper way."

My attention was whisked back to the cow. Where was the uterus? It had vanished. Again I started my frantic groping inside, and after pulling out the placenta, my fingers at last came upon the ragged edge of my incision. I drew as much as possible of the organ up to the light, where I noticed with sinking disquiet that my original opening had been enlarged to such an extent by the passage of that enormous calf that there was a long tear disappearing out of sight toward the cervix.

"Sutures." I held my hand out, and Norman gave me a fresh needle. "Hold the lips of the wound," I said, and began to stitch. I worked quickly until the tear ran out of sight. The rest was a kind of martyrdom. Norman hung on grimly while I stabbed at the invisible tissue far below.

Then to my dismay a further complication arose—the calf was now on his feet, blundering unsteadily around. The speed with which newly born animals get onto their legs has always fascinated me, but at this moment it was an unmitigated nuisance. The calf, looking for the udder with that instinct nobody can explain, kept pushing his nose at the cow's flank and at times went toppling headfirst into the gaping hole in her side.

"Reckon 'e wants back in again," Mr. Bushell said with a grin. "By 'eck, he's a wick un."

"Wick" is Yorkshire for lively, and the word was never more aptly applied. As I worked, I had to keep nudging the wet muzzle away with my elbow, but as fast as I pushed him back, the calf nosed in again, spreading particles of straw and dirt from the floor over the abdominal contents. "Look at that," I moaned. "As if there wasn't enough muck in there."

Norman didn't reply. Sweat ran down his blood-streaked face as he grappled with that unseen wound.

After an eternity I got as far down the uterine tear as I could, then we cleared away a lot of rubbish from the cow's abdomen and covered everything with antiseptic powder. I stitched up the muscle and skin layers, and at last the thing was finished. Norman and I got to our feet slowly, like two old men, and began to scrub and scrape ourselves clean.

Mr. Bushell left his position by the head and looked at the row of stitches. "Nice neat job," he said. "And a grand calf, too."

Yes, that was something. The little creature had dried off now, and he was a beauty, his body swaying on unsteady legs, his wide-set eyes filled with gentle curiosity. But that "neat job" hid things I didn't dare think about. I knew there was no hope for the cow. Still, as a gesture, I left the farmer some sulfa powders to give her three times a day. Then I got off the farm as quickly as I could.

We drove away in silence. I rounded a corner, then stopped the car under a tree and sank my head against the wheel. "Did you ever see such a performance?" I groaned. "All that muck in that poor cow—peritonitis is inevitable. And I'm pretty sure I've left a good-size hole in her uterus."

Norman spoke in a strangled undertone. "It was all my fault."

"No, it wasn't," I replied. "I am supposed to be a qualified veterinary surgeon, and I did nearly everything wrong. On top of it all, I shouted and nagged and behaved abominably toward you, and I owe you an apology."

"You didn't really. I—"

"Anyway, Norman," I broke in. "I want to thank you now. You worked like a Trojan and I'd have got nowhere without you. Let's go and have a pint."

At the village inn, we dropped into a quiet corner and pulled deeply at our beer glasses. We were both hot and weary and there didn't seem to be anything more to say.

I was sure I would never see Bella alive again, but first thing next morning a morbid curiosity made me ring Mr. Bushell.

"Oh, it's Mr. Herriot," he said. "Cow's up and eatin'."

It was several seconds before I was able to absorb his words. "Doesn't she look a bit dull or uncomfortable?" I asked huskily.

"Nay, nay, she's bright as a cricket. Finished off a rackful of hay, and I got a couple o' gallons of milk from 'er."

As if in a dream I heard his next question. "When'll you take them stitches out?"

"Stitches . . . ? Oh yes." I gave myself a shake. "In a fortnight, Mr. Bushell, in a fortnight."

After the horrors of the first visit, I was glad Norman was with me when I removed the sutures. There was no swelling around the wound, and Bella chewed her cud happily as I snipped away. In a pen nearby the calf gamboled and kicked his feet in the air.

"Has Bella shown any symptoms at all?" I couldn't help asking.

"Nay." The farmer shook his head slowly. "You wouldn't know owt had happened to 'er."

That was the way it was at my first cesarean. Over the years Bella went on to have eight more calves normally and unaided, a miracle that I can still hardly believe.

But Norman and I were not to know that. What we felt then was an elation all the sweeter for being unexpected. "Well, Norman," I said. "That's veterinary practice for you. You get a lot of nasty shocks, but some lovely surprises, too. I've often heard of the wonderful resistance of the bovine peritoneum, and thank heaven it's true."

"The whole thing's marvelous, isn't it?" he murmured dreamily. "I can't describe the way I feel. My head seems to be full of quotations like *While there is life there's hope.*"

"Yes, indeed," I said. "John Gay, isn't it? 'The Sick Man and the Angel.'"

Norman clapped his hands. "Oh, well done. Here's another good one: *Out of this nettle, danger, we pluck this flower, safety.*"

"Splendid, splendid," I replied. "Shakespeare, *Henry Fifth.*"

"No, *Henry Fourth.*"

I opened my mouth to argue, but Norman held up a confident hand. "It's no good, I'm right. And this time I *do* know what I'm talking about."

4

"Oooh . . . ooh-hoo-hooo!" The brokenhearted sobbing coming over the telephone jerked me fully awake. It was one a.m.

"Who is this?" I asked. "What on earth is the trouble?"

A man's voice pleaded between sobs. "It's Humphrey Cobb. Please come out and see Myrtle. I think she's dyin'."

"Myrtle?"

"Aye, me poor little dog. She's in a state, pantin' and gaspin'. Come quick! Oooh-hooo!"

"Where do you live?"

"Cedar House. End of Hill Street."

"I know it. I'll be there very soon."

"Oh, thank ye, thank ye. Myrtle hasn't got long. Hurry!"

As I leaped from the bed and pulled on my clothes, Helen sat up. "What is it, Jim?"

"Desperately urgent case. I have to hurry."

I galloped downstairs and out to the garage. I have always envied vets who stay relaxed under pressure. But I wasn't made that way. Cedar House was only a mile away, and I didn't have much time to think about the case before I arrived. In answer to my ring the porch light flashed on, and Humphrey Cobb stood before me. He was a small round man in his sixties with a Humpty-Dumpty appearance accentuated by a gleaming bald head.

"Oh, Mr. Herriot, come in," he cried brokenly as the tears streamed down his cheeks. "Thank ye for gettin' out of your bed to help me poor little Myrtle." As he spoke, the blast of whisky fumes almost made my head spin, and I noticed that as he preceded me into the kitchen he staggered slightly.

My patient was lying in a basket beside the stove in a large, well-appointed kitchen. I felt a warm surge when I saw that she was a beagle, like my own dog, Sam. I knelt down and looked at her closely. Her mouth was open and her tongue lolled, but she did not seem to be in acute distress. In fact, as I patted her head, her tail flapped against the blanket.

A heartrending wail sounded in my ear. "What d'ye make of

her, Mr. Herriot? It's her heart, isn't it?" The little man crouched over his pet, and the tears flowed unchecked.

"You know, Mr. Cobb, she doesn't seem all that bad to me. Don't upset yourself. Just give me a chance to examine her."

I placed my stethoscope over the ribs and listened to the steady thudding of a superbly strong heart. The temperature was normal, and I was palpating the abdomen when Mr. Cobb broke in again. "The trouble is," he gasped, "I neglect this poor animal. Ah've been all day at the races, gamblin' and drinkin', with never a thought for 'er."

"You left her alone all that time in the house?"

"Nay, nay, t'missus has been with her."

"Well, then." I felt I was getting out of my depth. "Wouldn't she feed Myrtle and let her out in the garden?"

"Oh aye," he said, wringing his hands. "But I shouldn't leave 'er. She thinks such a lot about me."

Suddenly I could feel one side of my face tingling with heat. My problem was solved. "You've got her too near the stove. She's panting because she's hot."

He looked at me doubtfully. "We just shifted 'er basket today. We've been gettin' some new tiles put down on the floor."

"Right," I said. "Shift it back again and she'll be fine."

"But, Mr. Herriot." His lips began to tremble again. "It's more than that. She's sufferin'. Look at her eyes."

Myrtle had the lovely big liquid eyes of her breed and she knew how to use them. Many people think the spaniel is number one when it comes to looking soulful, but I personally plump for the beagle. And Myrtle was an expert.

"Oh, I shouldn't worry about that, Mr. Cobb," I said. "Believe me, she'll be all right."

He was still unhappy. "But aren't ye going to do something?"

It was one of the great questions in veterinary practice. If you didn't "do something," people were not satisfied. And in this case Mr. Cobb was in greater need of treatment than his pet. So just to please him I produced a vitamin tablet from my bag and pushed it over the back of the little animal's tongue.

"There you are," I said. "I'm sure that will do her good."

"That's champion. You've set me mind at rest." Mr. Cobb led the way into a luxurious drawing room and tacked unsteadily toward a cocktail cabinet. "You'll 'ave a drink before you go?"

"No, really, thanks," I said. "I'd rather not."

"Well, I'll 'ave a drop. Just to steady me nerves." He tipped some whisky into a glass and waved me to a chair.

My bed was calling me, but I sat down and listened as he drank. He told me that he was a retired bookmaker from West Riding and that he had come to Darrowby only a month ago. Although no longer directly connected with horse racing, he still loved the sport and never missed a meeting in the north of England. "I get a taxi to take me and I have a right good day." His face was radiant as he recalled the happy times; then his woebegone expression returned. "But I neglect me dog. I leave her at home."

"Nonsense," I said. "You give her plenty of exercise?"

"Oh aye, lots of walks every day."

"Well, then, she really has a good life."

He beamed at me and sloshed out some more whisky. "Eee, you're a good lad. Come on, have one before you go."

"Oh, all right, just a small one, then."

As we drank he began gazing at me with something like devotion. "James Herriot," he slurred. "I suppose it'll be Jim, eh?"

"Well, yes."

"I'll call you Jim, then, and you can call me Humphrey."

"Okay, Humphrey," I said, and swallowed the last of my whisky. "But I really must go now."

Outside, he put a hand on my arm, his face serious again. "Thank ye, Jim. Myrtle was right bad tonight and I'm grateful."

Driving away, I realized that I had failed to convince him that I hadn't saved his dog's life. It had been an unusual visit and Humphrey Cobb was a very funny little man. But I liked him.

After that night I saw him frequently, exercising Myrtle in the fields. With his almost spherical build he seemed to bounce over the grass, but his manner was always self-contained and rational, except that he kept thanking me for pulling his dog back from the jaws of death.

Then quite suddenly I was back at the beginning. It was, once again, shortly after midnight when I lifted the bedside phone and heard the distraught weeping. "Oooh . . . oooh . . . Jim. Myrtle's in a bad way. Will ye come?"

"What . . . what is it this time?"

"She's twitchin' summat terrible. Oh, Jim, lad, don't keep me waiting. I'm worried to death. I'm sure she's got distemper." He broke down again.

My head began to reel. "She can't have distemper, Humphrey. Not in a flash, like that."

"I'm beggin' you, Jim," he went on, as though he hadn't heard.

"All right," I said wearily. "I'll be there in a few minutes."

"Oh, you're a good lad, Jim. . . ." The voice trailed away as I replaced the phone. I dressed with none of the panic of the first time. It must be another false alarm—but you never knew.

At Cedar House, the same dizzying wave of whisky fumes enveloped me on the porch. Humphrey, sniffling and moaning, ushered me into the kitchen. "There she is," he said, pointing to her basket. "I've just got back from Ripon and found 'er like this."

"Racing again, eh?"

"Aye, gamblin' and drinkin' and leavin' me poor dog pinin' at home. I'm a rotter, Jim, that's what I am."

"Rubbish, Humphrey! I've told you before. You're not doing her any harm by having a day out. Anyway, how about this twitching? She looks all right now."

"Yes, she's stopped doin' it, but when I came in, her back leg was goin' like this." He made a jerking movement with his hand.

I groaned inwardly. "But she could have been scratching."

"Nay, there's summat more than that. I can tell she's sufferin'. Just look at them eyes."

Myrtle's beagle eyes were pools of emotion, and it was easy to read melting reproach in their depths.

With a feeling of futility I examined her. I knew what I would find—nothing. But when I tried to explain that his pet was normal, Humphrey wouldn't have it.

"Give her a tablet," he pleaded. "It cured her last time."

I felt I had to pacify him, so Myrtle received another vitamin.

Immensely relieved, Humphrey wove his way to the drawing room and the whisky bottle.

"I need a little pick-me-up after that shock," he said. "You'll 'ave one, too, won't you, Jim, lad?"

This melodrama was enacted frequently over the next few months, always after race meetings and always between midnight and one a.m. I had ample opportunity to analyze the situation, and I came to a fairly obvious conclusion: most of the time Humphrey was a normal conscientious pet owner, but after a large intake of alcohol his affectionate feelings degenerated into sentimentality and guilt. I invariably went out when he called me because I knew that he would be deeply distressed if I refused. I was treating Humphrey, not Myrtle. It amused me that not once did he accept my protestations that my visit was unnecessary. Each time he was sure that my magic tablets had saved his dog's life.

Mind you, I did not discount the possibility that Myrtle was deliberately working on him with those eyes. The canine mind is quite capable of disapproval. I took my own dog almost everywhere with me, but if I left him at home and went with Helen to the cinema, he would lie under our bed, sulking.

I quailed when Humphrey told me he had decided to have Myrtle mated, because I knew that the ensuing pregnancy would be laden with harassment for me. And that was how it turned out. The little man flew into a series of unfounded panics, discovering imaginary symptoms in Myrtle regularly throughout the nine weeks. I was vastly relieved when she gave birth to five healthy pups. Now, I thought, I would get some peace. I was just about tired of Humphrey's nocturnal nonsense.

Then late one night soon afterward, the phone exploded in my ear. As I picked up the receiver, the "Oooh . . . oooh . . . oooh!" was only too familiar.

I clenched my teeth. "Humphrey! What is it this time?"

"Oh, Jim, Myrtle's really dyin', I know she is. Come quick!"

"Dying?" I took a couple of rasping breaths. "How do you make that out?"

"Well . . . she's stretched out on 'er side, tremblin'."

"Anything else?"

"Aye, t'missus said Myrtle's been lookin' worried and walkin' stiff when she let her out this afternoon. I'm not long back from Redcar, ye see."

"So you've been to the races, eh?"

"That's right . . . neglectin' me dog. I'm nothing but a scamp."

I closed my eyes. There was no end to the imaginary symptoms. Trembling this time, looking worried, walking stiff. What would it be next? I have always made a point of never refusing to make a call at night, but Humphrey had stretched this principle to the breaking point. This couldn't go on. I had to make a stand.

"Look, Humphrey," I said. "There's nothing wrong with your dog. I've told you again and again. . . ."

"Oh, Jim, lad, don't be long. Oooh-hooo!"

"I'm not coming, Humphrey."

"Nay, don't say that! She's goin' fast, I tell ye!"

"I mean it. It's just wasting my time and your money, so go to bed. Myrtle will be fine."

Tormented by remorse at refusing to go out for the first time in my life, I fell into an uneasy slumber. But it is a good thing that the subconscious mind works on during sleep, because with the alarm clock reading two thirty a.m., I came suddenly wide awake. "Oh no!" I cried. "Myrtle's got eclampsia!" I scrambled from the bed and began to throw on my clothes.

"What is it?" asked Helen. "What's the matter?"

"Humphrey Cobb!" I gasped, tying a shoelace.

"Humphrey . . . but you said there was never any hurry. . . ."

"There is this time. His dog's dying." I glared again at the clock. "In fact, she could be dead now."

I fled out to the car with my brain spelling out the concise case history that Humphrey had given me: small bitch nursing puppies, signs of anxiety and stiff gait this afternoon, and now prostrate and trembling. Classic puerperal eclampsia. Rapidly fatal without treatment. And it was nearly an hour and a half since he had phoned. I couldn't bear to think about it.

Humphrey was still up. He had obviously been consoling himself with the bottle, because he could barely stand.

"You've come, Jim, lad," he mumbled, blinking at me.

"Yes, how is she?"

"Just t'same. . . ."

Clutching my calcium and my intravenous syringe, I rushed past him into the kitchen. Myrtle's sleek body was extended in a tetanic spasm. She was gasping for breath, quivering violently, and bubbles of saliva dripped from her mouth. Those eyes had lost their softness and were fixed in a frantic stare. She looked terrible, but she was alive. . . . She was alive.

I lifted the squealing pups onto a nearby rug and quickly clipped and swabbed the area over the radial vein. Calcium was the cure for this condition, but a quick blast would surely kill the patient. I inserted a needle into the blood vessel and slowly depressed the plunger. Some of these cases needed narcotics as well as calcium, and I had Nembutal and morphine ready at hand.

But as the time passed, Myrtle's breathing slowed down and the rigid muscles began to relax. When she started to swallow her saliva and look around at me, I knew she would live.

I was waiting for the last tremors to disappear from her limbs when I felt a tap on my shoulder. Humphrey was standing there with the whisky bottle.

"You'll 'ave one, won't you, Jim?"

I didn't need much persuading, knowing that I had almost been responsible for Myrtle's death. I had barely taken the first sip when the little animal got up from the basket and walked over to inspect her pups. Some eclampsias are slow to respond, but others are spectacularly quick, and I was grateful for the sake of my nervous system that this was one of the quick ones. In fact, the recovery was almost uncanny, because, after sniffing her family, Myrtle walked over to greet me, her eyes brimming with friendliness and her tail waving.

I was stroking her ears when Humphrey broke into a giggle. "You know, Jim, I've learned summat tonight," he drawled.

"What's that, Humphrey?"

"I've learned . . . hee-hee-hee . . . I've learned what a silly feller I've been all these months."

"How do you mean?"

He wagged a forefinger sagely. "Well, you've allus been tellin' me I was imaginin' things when I thought me dog was ill."

"Yes," I said. "That's right."

"And I never believed you, did I? Well, now I know you were right. I've been nobbut a fool." He waved a hand toward his bright-faced, tail-wagging little dog. "Just look at her. Anybody can see there was never anythin' wrong with Myrtle tonight."

5

IT WAS a quiet moment in Skeldale House, and I was thinking back to the old bachelor days when my partner, Siegfried, his student brother, Tristan, and I all lived under that roof.

"You know, Jim," I remember Tristan saying on one of those long-ago mornings, "I often wonder if there is any other household where the mark of a lady's favor is expressed in goat manure."

"Well, isn't that funny," I'd said to Tristan on that occasion. "I've been thinking the same thing. It certainly is rather an odd business."

We had just come from the breakfast table. Mrs. Hall, our housekeeper, had always placed our letters next to our plates, and there, at Siegfried's place, dominating the scene like an emblem of triumph, stood the tin of goat droppings from Miss Grantley. We all knew what it was, despite its wrapping of brown paper, because she always used the same type of container— an empty cocoa tin about six inches high. Either she collected them from friends or she was very fond of cocoa.

One indisputable thing was that she was very fond of goats. They seemed almost to rule her existence, which was strange, because the care of goats was an unlikely hobby for a blond beauty who could have stepped effortlessly into the film world.

Another odd thing about Miss Grantley was that she had never married. Each time I had been at her house I had marveled that anybody like her was able to keep the men away. She would be about thirty, with a nicely rounded figure and elegant legs, and sometimes when I looked at the fine contours of her face I wondered whether that rather firm jaw might have frightened prospective suitors. But no, she was cheerful and charming; I decided that she just didn't want to get married. She had a lovely home and obviously plenty of money. She appeared to be perfectly happy.

There was no doubt at all that the goat droppings were a mark of favor. Miss Grantley took her stockkeeping very seriously and insisted on regular laboratory examination of feces samples for parasites. These samples were always addressed to Siegfried, and I had attached no importance to this until one morning, a few days after I had pleased her immensely by removing an embedded piece of chaff from one of her billies' eyes, the familiar tin appeared by my breakfast plate addressed to me.

That was when I realized it was a gesture of approval. In ancient days a feudal knight would carry a glove at his saddle bow or a scarf on his lance point as a symbol of his lady's esteem. With Miss Grantley it was goat droppings.

On the occasion when I got mine, Siegfried's face showed the slightest flicker of surprise and I suppose I might have shown a trace of smugness, but he needn't have worried. Within a week or two the tin reappeared at his end of the table. And after all, it was the natural thing, because if sheer male attractiveness entered into this situation, there was no doubt that Siegfried was out in front by a street. Tristan pursued the local girls enthusiastically and with considerable success; I had no reason to complain about my share of female company, but Siegfried was in a different class. He seemed to drive women mad.

He didn't have to chase them; they chased him. I hadn't known him long before I realized that the tales I had heard about the irresistible appeal of tall, lean-faced men were true. And when you added his natural charm and commanding personality, it was inevitable that the goat droppings would land regularly by his plate. In fact, that is how it was for a long time, even though Tristan and I paid almost as many visits to Miss Grantley's goats as Siegfried, because she called us out for the slightest ailment.

However, when I heard her voice on the telephone one morning, I knew that this time it wasn't for something trivial.

She sounded agitated. "Mr. Herriot, Tina has caught her shoulder on a nail and torn herself badly. Can you come out immediately?"

"Yes, as it happens, I can. I'll leave right away."

A mild glow of satisfaction rippled through me. This would be just another stitching job, and I liked stitching. It was easy and always impressed the client. I would be on happier ground there than when Miss Grantley was quizzing me about goat diseases. They had taught me practically nothing about goats at college, and though I had read up on them, I was no expert.

I was leaving the room when Tristan levered himself slowly from the depths of the armchair where he spent a lot of his time. He yawned and stretched. "Miss Grantley's, eh? Think I'll come, too. Just feel like a ride out."

I smiled. "Okay, come on, then." He was always good company.

Miss Grantley met us in a silky, pale blue coverall that did nothing to diminish her attractions.

"Thank you so much for coming," she said. "Please follow me."

Following her was rewarding. In fact, on entering the goat house Tristan failed to see the step and fell onto his knees. Miss Grantley glanced at him briefly before hurrying to a pen at the far end.

"There she is," she said, and put a hand over her eyes. "I can't bear to look."

Tina was a fine white Saanen, but her beauty was ravaged by a huge laceration that had pulled the skin down from her shoulder in a long V, exposing the muscles down to the bone. It was a mess, but all superficial, and I could easily put it right and look very good in the process. Already I could see myself inserting the last stitch and pointing to the now almost invisible wound. "There now, that looks a lot better, doesn't it?" Miss Grantley would be in raptures.

Now she wrung her hands. "Do you think you can save her?"

"Oh yes." I nodded weightily. "It will be a big stitching job, but I feel sure she will pull through."

"Oh, thank heaven." She sighed, relieved. "I'll fetch hot water."

Soon I was ready for action. Tristan held Tina's head while I cleaned the area thoroughly and began to stitch. Miss Grantley

passed me the scissors to clip each suture. It was a nice smooth start, but it was a large wound and it would take some time. I searched my mind for light conversation.

Tristan chipped in, apparently thinking the same thing. "Wonderful animal, the goat," he said lightly.

"Ah yes." Miss Grantley gave him a bright smile. "I agree."

"When you think about it, they are probably the earliest domestic animals," he went on. "Cave paintings from prehistoric days show that they have been part of the world of man since recorded time. It is a fascinating thought."

From my squatting position I looked up at him in surprise. In my relationship with Tristan I had discovered several things that fascinated him, but goats were not one of them.

"And they have such a marvelous metabolism," he added. "They consume food other animals won't look at, and they produce abundant milk from that food."

"Yes, indeed," breathed Miss Grantley.

Tristan laughed. "They're such characters, too. Tough and hardy under all climatic conditions, absolutely fearless, and they can eat with impunity many poisonous plants that would kill most creatures."

"Oh, they *are* amazing." Miss Grantley gazed at my friend and passed the scissors to me without turning her head.

I felt I ought to make some contribution. "Goats certainly are extremely—" I began.

"But really, you know"—Tristan was in full flow again—"the thing that appeals to me most about them is their affectionate nature. Clearly that is why people become so attached to them."

Miss Grantley nodded gravely. "How true, how true."

My colleague stretched out a hand and fingered the hay in the animal's rack. "I see you feed them properly—thistles, bits of shrubs and coarse plants. Obviously you know that goats prefer rough stuff to grass. No wonder your animals are so healthy."

"Oh, thank you." She blushed faintly. "Of course I give them concentrates, too."

"Whole grain, I hope?"

"Oh yes, always."

"Good, good. Keeps up the pH of the rumen. Goats can get hypertrophy of the rumenal walls and inhibition of cellulose-digesting bacteria with a low pH."

Miss Grantley was staring at him as if he were a prophet.

"Can I have the scissors, please?" I grunted. I was beginning to feel cramped in my bent-over position and also a little piqued at the growing impression that my client had forgotten all about me. But I stitched on doggedly, one half of my mind watching thankfully as the skin gradually covered the denuded area, the other listening in amazement as Tristan pontificated on the construction of goat houses, their dimensions and ventilation.

A long time later I inserted the last suture and straightened up wearily. "Well now, that looks better, doesn't it?" I said, but it didn't have the impact I expected, because Tristan and my client were deeply involved in a discussion of the relative merits of the different breeds of goats.

Miss Grantley suddenly became aware that I had finished. "Oh, thank you," she said absently. "You have taken such pains. Now you must both come in for coffee."

As we balanced our cups on our knees in the elegant sitting room, Tristan carried on unabated, dealing in depth with the feeding of weaned kids and anesthesia for dehorning. Then Miss Grantley turned toward me. She was clearly still under his spell but no doubt felt that it would be only polite to bring me into the conversation.

"Mr. Herriot, one thing worries me. I share a pasture with the farmer next door, and my goats graze with his sheep. Now, I have heard that his animals are troubled with coccidiosis. Is there any chance that my goats could contract it from them?"

I took a long pull at my coffee cup to give myself time to think. "Well . . . er . . . I would say—"

My friend broke in again effortlessly. "Most unlikely. You don't need to worry on that account. Most types of coccidiosis are specific to their individual hosts."

"Thank you." Miss Grantley addressed me again, as though deciding to give me a last chance. "How about worms, Mr. Herriot? Can my goats become infected with worms from the sheep?"

"Ah now, let's see. . . ." I could feel a light perspiration breaking out on my brow. "The thing is—"

"Quite so," murmured Tristan, gliding once more to my aid. "As Mr. Herriot was about to say, there is a very real danger of infection with helminthiasis, since the common nematodes are the same in both species. You must always worm regularly, and if I can give you a brief program . . ."

I sank deeper in my chair and let him get on with it. It came to an end at last, and we went out to the car.

"I'll come back in ten days to remove the stitches," I said to Miss Grantley. It struck me that it was just about the only sensible thing I had said.

I drove a few hundred yards along the road, then I stopped the car and turned to my companion.

"Since when have you been a goat lover?" I demanded bitterly. "And where the hell did you get all that high-powered stuff you were preaching back there?"

Tristan giggled, then threw back his head and laughed immoderately. "Sorry, Jim," he said when he had recovered. "I have exams coming up in a few weeks, as you know, and I heard that one of the examiners is really goat-oriented. Last night I boned up on every bit of goat literature I could find. Uncanny how I had the opportunity to trot it all out so soon after."

"I see," I said. "You'd better let me see those things you read last night. I didn't realize I was so ignorant."

There was an interesting little sequel about a week later. Siegfried and I were going in to breakfast when my partner stopped in mid-stride and stared at the table. The familiar brown-wrapped cocoa tin was there, but this time it was at his brother's place. Slowly he walked over and examined the label. I had a look, too, and there was no mistake. It was addressed to "Mr. Tristan Farnon."

Siegfried said nothing but sat down at the head of the table. Soon the young man himself joined us, examined the tin with interest and started on his meal.

No one said a word, but the undeniable fact hung heavy in the room. Tristan—for the moment at least—was top man.

6

THE farmer moved between the cows and took hold of my patient's tail, and when I saw the man's haircut, I knew immediately that Josh Anderson had been on the job again. It was a Sunday morning, and everything fitted into place.

"Were you in the Hare and Pheasant last night?" I inquired carelessly as I inserted a thermometer in the cow.

The farmer ran a hand ruefully over his head. "Aye. I should've known better, pickin' a Saturday night."

Josh Anderson was one of the local barbers. He liked his job, but he also liked his beer. In fact, he took his scissors and clippers to the pub with him every night. For the price of a pint, he would give anybody a quick trim in the gents' lavatory. With beer at sixpence a pint it was good value, but Josh's clients knew they were taking a chance. If the barber's intake had been moderate, they would escape relatively unscathed—the standard of hair-styling in Darrowby was not fastidious—but if he had imbibed more than his usual eight pints, as he did on Saturday nights, terrible things could happen.

I looked again at the farmer's head. From my experience I judged that Josh could have been around the ten-pint mark when he did that one. The upper hair seemed to have been delved into at random, leaving bare patches in some parts and long, dangling wisps in others. No doubt the back would be interesting, too; there could be a pigtail or anything lurking there.

Yes, I decided, definitely a ten-pinter. After twelve to fourteen pints, Josh was inclined to cast away all caution and simply run over his victim's head with the clippers, leaving a tuft in front— the classic convict's crop that necessitated wearing a cap for several weeks thereafter.

I always played safe; when my hair needed cutting, I went to Josh's shop, where he operated in strict sobriety.

I was sitting there a few days later, waiting my turn with my dog, Sam, under my seat. There was a burly man in the barber chair, and his red face, reflected in the mirror, was contorted every few seconds with spasms of pain. Because the simple fact was that Josh didn't cut hair, he pulled it out. He did this not only because his equipment was antiquated and needed sharpening, but because he had perfected a certain flick of the wrist with his hand clippers, which wrenched the hairs from their follicles at the end of each stroke.

The wonder was that anybody went to Josh for a haircut, because there was another barber close by. Perhaps it was that everybody liked him.

Sitting there in his shop, I looked at him as he worked. He was a tiny man in his fifties with a gentle smile that never seemed to leave his face; that smile and his big, curiously unworldly eyes gave him an unusual attraction. As his client rose from the chair, patently relieved to have his ordeal over, Josh fussed around him, brushing him down and chattering gaily. You could see his obvious love of his fellowmen.

Next to his burly client, Josh looked smaller than ever, and I marveled at how he managed to accommodate all that beer. Even now, after forty years in Yorkshire, I cannot compete. Maybe it is my Glasgow upbringing, but after two or three pints discomfort sets in. The remarkable thing is that throughout the years I can hardly recall seeing a Yorkshireman drunk. They become progressively more jovial as the long cascade goes down their throats, but they seldom fall about or do anything silly. Josh, for instance, would swallow around eight pints every night of the week, except Saturday, when he stepped up his intake to between ten and fourteen, yet he never looked much different. His professional skill suffered, but that was all.

He was turning to me now. "Well, Mr. Herriot, it's good to see you again." He warmed me with his smile and those wide almost mystic eyes as he ushered me to the chair. "Are you well?"

"I'm fine, thank you, Mr. Anderson," I replied. "And you?"

"Nicely, sir, nicely." He began to tuck the sheet under my chin, then laughed delightedly as my little beagle trotted in under the folds. "By gum, Mr. Herriot, Sam's a faithful friend. Never lets you out of 'is sight if he can help it."

"That's right," I said. "And I don't like to go anywhere without him." I swiveled around in my chair. "By the way, didn't I see you with a dog the other day?"

Josh paused, scissors in hand. "You did an' all. A little stray. Got 'er from the Cat and Dog Home at York and she's a grand un. Now that our kids have all left home, t'missus and I fancied gettin' a dog, and we think the world of her."

"What breed is she?"

"Eee, now you're askin'. Nobbut a mongrel, I reckon. I can't see any pedigree about her, but money wouldn't buy 'er. Hang on a minute and I'll bring 'er down."

He clumped upstairs, to where he lived above the shop, and returned with a little bitch in his arms. "There you are, Mr. Herriot. What d'you think of that?" He stood her on the floor for my inspection.

The little animal looked like a miniature Wensleydale sheep, light gray in color, with long, crinkled hair. Definitely a hound of baffling lineage, but the swishing tail bore witness to her good nature.

"I like her," I said. "I think you've picked a winner."

"That's what we think." He stooped and fondled his new pet, picking up the long hairs and rubbing them gently between finger and thumb. It looked a little odd, then it occurred to me that that was what he was used to doing with his human customers. "We've called her Venus," he said.

"Venus?"

"Aye, because she's so beautiful." His tone was serious.

"Ah yes," I said. "I see."

He washed his hands, took up his scissors and grasped a few strands of my hair. Again he went through the procedure of rubbing the hairs between his fingers before cutting them.

I couldn't understand why he did this, but I was too preoccupied to give the matter much thought. I felt an uncomfortable tug as the scissors' blunt edges came together. Still, it wasn't too bad until he reached for the clippers; then I gripped the arms of the chair as though I were at the dentist's. That jerk at the end, plucking the last tuft from its roots, set me grimacing at the mirror. Once or twice an involuntary "Ooh!" or "Aah!" escaped me, but Josh gave no sign of having heard; never had I seen him react to his customers' stifled cries of pain.

Though he was the least arrogant of men, Josh considered himself a gifted hairdresser. Even now, as he gave me a final combing, I could see the pride shining from his face. Head on one side, he made a finicky snip here and there before holding up the hand mirror for my inspection. "All right, Mr. Herriot?"

"Lovely, Mr. Anderson." Relief added warmth to my voice.

"Aye, you know, it's easy to cut hair off. The secret is knowin' what to leave on."

I had heard him say it a hundred times before, but I laughed dutifully as he whisked his brush over the back of my coat.

My hair used to grow pretty fast, but I didn't need to pay another visit to the barber before he arrived at my door one day carrying Venus in his arms. She was a vastly different creature from the placid little animal I had seen in his shop. She was bubbling saliva, retching and pawing frantically at her face.

"Tell me what's happened, Mr. Anderson. Has she swallowed something?"

"Aye, a chicken bone." Josh looked distraught.

"A chicken bone! Don't you know you should never give a dog chicken bones?"

"Aye, ah know, ah know, but we'd had a bird for our dinner and she pinched the frame out of the dustbin. She had a good crunch at it afore I spotted 'er, and now she's goin' to choke!" He was on the verge of tears.

"Now just calm down," I said. "I don't think Venus is choking. By the way she's pawing, I'd say something's stuck in her mouth."

I forced her jaws apart and saw—with a surge of relief—a long bone sliver jammed tightly between the back molars, forming a bar across the roof of the mouth. This was a common occurrence in practice, easily relieved by a flick of the forceps.

I put my hand on the barber's shoulder. "You can stop worrying, Mr. Anderson, it's just a bone stuck in her teeth. Come into the consulting room and I'll have it out in a jiffy."

I could see the man relaxing as we walked to the back of the house. "Oh, thank God for that, Mr. Herriot. I thought she'd had it, honest, I did. And we've grown right fond of the little thing. I couldn't bear to lose 'er."

"No question of that, I assure you." I put the dog on the table and reached for my forceps. "This won't take a minute."

Jimmy, now five, had trailed after us, and he watched with mild interest as I poised the instrument. Even at his age, he had seen this sort of thing many times and it wasn't very exciting. But you never knew in veterinary practice; it was worth hanging around, because funny things could happen. He put his hands in his pockets and rocked back and forth on his heels, whistling softly as he watched me.

Usually it is simply a matter of opening the mouth, clamping the forceps on the bone and removing it. But Venus recoiled in terror from the gleaming metal and so did the barber. I tried to be soothing. "This is nothing, Mr. Anderson. I'm not going to hurt her in the least. Just hold her head firmly for a moment."

He took a deep breath, grasped the dog's neck and shut his eyes. Venus struggled violently, pawing at my hand to the accompaniment of her owner's moans. When I did get the forceps into her mouth, she locked her front teeth on the instrument and hung on fiercely. Finally Mr. Anderson could stand it no longer and let go. The little dog leaped to the floor while Jimmy watched appreciatively.

"Let's have another go," I said to the barber.

Josh bent and extended trembling hands toward his dog, but each time he touched her she slithered away until, with a great shuddering sigh, he flopped face down on the tiles. Jimmy giggled. Things were looking up.

I helped the barber to his feet. "I tell you what, Mr. Anderson. I'll cut out this struggling with a short-acting anesthetic."

Josh paled. "Put her to sleep? Will she be all right?"

"Of course. Just leave her to me and come back for her in an hour. She'll be able to walk then." I began to steer him out. "We'll only upset her if we go on this way."

"Very well, then. I'll go along to me brother's for an hour."

"Splendid." I waited till I heard the front door close behind him, then quickly made up a dose of Pentothal. Dogs do not put on such a tough front when their owners are not present, and I scooped Venus easily from the floor onto the table. I slid the needle into a vein and within seconds she was asleep.

"No trouble now, Jimmy, lad," I said. I pushed the teeth apart effortlessly, gripped the bone with the forceps and lifted it from the mouth. "Lovely. All done."

I dropped the bone into the waste bin. "Yes, my boy. That's the professional way to do it. No undignified scrambling."

My son nodded briefly. Events had gone dull again. He had been hoping for great things when Mr. Anderson draped himself on our floor, but this was tame stuff. He had stopped smiling.

My own satisfied smile had become a little fixed. I was watching Venus carefully, and she wasn't breathing. I tried to ignore the lurch in my stomach, because I have always been a nervous anesthetist. I told myself there was no danger. She had received the correct dose, and you often get this reaction with Pentothal. But just the same I wished to God she would start breathing.

The heart was still going all right. I depressed the ribs a few times—nothing. I touched the unseeing eyeball—no corneal reflex. As I stared closely at Venus, I could tell that Jimmy was watching me keenly, his unerring instinct for the unpredictable aroused.

His hunch was proved right when I suddenly lifted Venus from the table, shook her vainly a few times above my head, then set off at full gallop along the passage. I could hear the eager shuffle of Jimmy's slippers just behind me.

I threw open the side door and shot into the back garden. The little dog's ribs still were not moving and the eyes stared sightlessly ahead. Oh, this just couldn't happen!

I seized Venus by a hind leg in either hand and began to whirl her around my head, attaining a remarkable speed as I put all my strength into the swing. This method of resuscitation seems to have gone out of fashion now, but it was very much in vogue then. It certainly met with the full approval of my son. In his ignorant glee over his father's funny behavior, he laughed so much that he fell down and sprawled on the grass. When I stopped and glared at the still immobile ribs, he cried, "Again, Daddy, again." And he didn't have to wait more than a few seconds before Daddy was in full action once more, with Venus swooping through the air like a bird on the wing.

It exceeded all Jimmy's expectations. How gloriously he had been rewarded. To this day the scene is vivid: my tension and misery lest my patient should die, and in the background the helpless, high-pitched laughter of my son.

I don't know how many times I stopped, then recommenced my whirling; but at last, at one of the intervals, the chest wall gave a heave and the eyes blinked. With a gasp of relief I collapsed face down on the cool turf and peered through the green blades as the breathing became regular and Venus began to lick her lips and look around.

Jimmy was disappointed. "Aren't you going to do any more?"

"No, son, no." I sat up and dragged Venus onto my lap. "It's all over now."

"Well, that was funny. Why did you do it?"

"To make the dog breathe."

"Do you always do that to make them breathe?"

"No, thank heaven, not often." I got slowly to my feet and carried Venus back to the consulting room.

By the time Josh Anderson arrived, his pet was looking almost normal. "She's still a little unsteady from the anesthetic," I said. "But that won't last long."

"Eee, isn't that grand! And that nasty bone, is it . . . ?"

"All gone, Mr. Anderson." I opened her mouth. "You see? Not a thing."

He smiled happily. "Did ye have any bother with her?"

I swallowed. To tell him that his dog had been almost dead for a considerable time would not cheer him, nor would it bolster his faith in me. Out came the whitest of lies: "A quite uneventful operation, Mr. Anderson."

"Wonderful, wonderful. I am grateful, Mr. Herriot." He bent over the dog, and again I noticed the strange rolling of the strands of hair between his fingers.

"Have ye been floatin' through the air, Venus?" he murmured.

The back of my neck prickled. "What . . . makes you ask?"

He turned his eyes up to me, those eyes with their unworldly depths. "Well . . . I reckon she'd think she was floatin' while she was asleep. Just a funny feeling I had."

"Ah yes, well, er . . . right." I had a very funny feeling myself. "You'd better take her home now and keep her quiet for the rest of the day."

When he left I was very thoughtful: floating . . . floating.

A fortnight later I was again seated in Josh's barber chair. Usually he began with the scissors, but today he started straight in with the dread clippers. In an attempt to alleviate the pain, I began to chatter. "How is—ouch—Venus getting on?"

"Oh fine, fine." Josh smiled at me tenderly in the mirror as he whipped out another tuft with that inimitable flick of his. "The thing is, Mr. Herriot, it's grand to 'ave faith in your vet. I knew our little pet was in good 'ands."

"It's—aaah—nice to hear that." Tired of trying to speak while he tugged away, I made an effort to concentrate on something else—a trick I adopt at the dentist's. I thought as hard as I could about my garden at Skeldale House; the lawns really did want mowing, and there were all those weeds to get at when I had a minute to spare. I had got around to considering whether it was time to put some fertilizer on my tomatoes when the barber's voice pulled me back to reality.

"Mr. Herriot." He was twiddling away at a wisp of my hair with his fingers. "I like gardening, too."

I almost jumped from the chair. "That's remarkable! I was just thinking about my garden."

"Aye, ah know." His eyes had a faraway look as he rolled and rolled with finger and thumb. "It comes through the hair, ye know. Your thoughts. They come through to me."

"What!"

"Yes. Well, just think about it, Mr. Herriot. Them hairs go right down into your head, and they catch summat from your brain and send it up to me."

"Oh really, you're kidding me." I gave a loud laugh that nevertheless had a hollow ring.

Josh shook his head. "No, I'm not jokin' nor jestin', Mr. Herriot. I've been at this game for forty years, and it keeps happenin' to me. You'd be flabbergasted if I told ye some of the thoughts that's come up. Couldn't repeat 'em, I tell ye."

I slumped lower in my white sheet. Absolute rubbish and nonsense, of course. But I made a firm resolve never to think of Venus' anesthetic during a haircut.

7

"This is Biggins 'ere."

I gripped the telephone tightly. Mr. Biggins' vacillations always tried me sorely. He regarded calling out the vet as a final desperate measure, and it was sheer torture for him to make up his mind to do it. On top of that, he was extremely pigheaded about taking my advice when I did go to his farm, and I knew beyond doubt that I had never managed to please him.

He had made me suffer during my pre-RAF days, and now, with the war well over, he was still there, a bit older and a bit more pigheaded.

"What's the trouble, Mr. Biggins?" I asked.

"Well . . . I 'ave a heifer badly."

"Right, I'll have a look at her this morning."

"Haud on, just a minute." Mr. Biggins was still not sure he wanted me there. "Are you sure she needs seein'?"

"Well, I don't know. What is she doing?"

"She's been off her grub for a week, and now . . ." There was a long pause. "She's just laid out, like."

"That sounds serious," I said. "I'll be along as soon as possible."

"Ah, but . . . but . . . are ye sure there's any need . . . ?"

I put down the receiver. I knew from hard experience that

this conversation could go on for a long time. I also knew that I was probably visiting a hopeless case, but if I got there immediately, I might be able to do something.

I was on the farm within ten minutes, and Mr. Biggins met me with his typical attitude—hands in pockets, shoulders hunched, eyes regarding me suspiciously from under a thick fringe of graying eyebrows. "Ye're ower late," he grunted.

I stopped with one foot out of the car. "You mean she's dead?"

"Nay, but just about. Ye're too late to do owt now."

I gritted my teeth. This animal had been ill for a week, I had arrived ten minutes after being summoned, but the farmer's tone was unequivocal; if it died it would be my fault.

"Ah well," I said, trying to relax. "If she's dying, there's nothing I can do." I began to get back into the car.

Mr. Biggins lowered his head and kicked at a cobblestone. "Are ye not going to look at 'er while you're 'ere?"

"I will, if that's what you want." I climbed out again.

He hesitated. "Will ye charge me extra?"

"No, I won't. I've made the journey here, and if I can't do anything more, that's all you'll pay for."

The sight in the fold yard was sadly familiar: the skinny young beast lying in a deep coma, eyes glazed and moving every few seconds with the slow nystagmus of approaching death.

"Yes, you're right, Mr. Biggins," I said. "She's dying." I picked up my bag and began to leave.

The farmer gave me a truculent stare. "So you're just goin' to walk away without doin' owt? I've allus heard that where there's life, there's hope."

"Not in this case, I assure you. But if you like, I can try a stimulant injection."

"It's not what ah like. You're t'one that's supposed to know."

"Very well, I'll have a try," I said. But as I slipped the needle in and depressed the plunger, Mr. Biggins gave tongue again.

"Expensive things, injections. How much will this cost me?"

"I honestly don't know." My brain was beginning to reel.

"You'll know awright when you get t'pen in your 'and to send me that big bill, won't ye?"

I didn't answer. As the last drop of fluid trickled into the vein, the heifer extended her forelimbs, stared sightlessly ahead for a second, then stopped breathing. I put my hand over her heart. "I'm afraid she's dead, Mr. Biggins."

The farmer rubbed his chin. "Well, you've wasted me money with that injection. What was t'matter with 'er?"

"I don't know. You would need a postmortem examination to find the cause."

The farmer began to pluck excitedly at his coat. "Well, this is a funny carry-on. I 'ave a dead beast here, and nobody knows what killed her. Could be anything. Could be anthrax!"

"Oh no, Mr. Biggins. Anthrax is very sudden, and you say this heifer was ill for over a week."

"Nay, nay, not right ill. Just a bit off, then she went down like a shot at t'end. That was sudden enough! And Fred Bramley along t'road had a beast wi' anthrax last month, didn't he? The Darrowby and Houlton *Times* was on about it, and they said that all sudden deaths should be examined for anthrax because it was fatal to people." Mr. Biggins stuck his jaw out. "I want ma heifer examined!"

"Okay," I replied wearily. "If you say so. As it happens, I've brought my microscope with me."

"Microscope? That sounds costly. How much will that be?"

"That's all right, the Ministry pays me," I said, and began to walk toward the house.

Mr. Biggins raised his voice. "Where you goin' now?"

"Inside. I've got to use your phone to report to the Ministry. I can't do anything till I get permission."

He stood by me as I spoke to the Ministry clerk, impatiently fidgeting as I asked him for the proper name of the farm and the breed of the heifer. "Didn't know ah'd have to go through all this," he mumbled.

I went out and got my postmortem knife. I made a nick at the root of the heifer's tail, smeared some blood onto a glass slide and took this, along with the microscope, into the farmhouse kitchen. I fixed the film of blood by drawing it through the flames in the hearth, then moved to the sink and poured methylene blue over the slide. In the process a small blue pool formed in the white sink bottom, and the coloration stayed there after I had swilled the slide with water from the tap.

"Look at that!" Mr. Biggins exclaimed. "You've stained t'sink. The missus'll play 'ell when she gets home this afternoon."

I forced a smile. "Don't worry, it will come off easily." But I could see he didn't believe me.

I dried the slide off at the fire, rigged up the microscope and peered through the eyepiece. As I expected, not an anthrax bacillus in sight. "Well, there's nothing there," I said. "You can call the knacker man quite safely."

Mr. Biggins made a long-suffering gesture. "All that fuss for nothin'."

As I drove away I felt, not for the first time, that you couldn't win with Mr. Biggins, and the conviction was strengthened a month later when he came into the surgery. "One of me cows has wooden tongue," he announced. "I want some iodine to paint on."

Siegfried looked up from the daybook, where he was checking the visits. "Oh, you're a bit out of date, Mr. Biggins," he said, smiling. "That treatment went out years ago. We've got far better medicine now—sulfanilamide."

The farmer took his usual stance, head down, glowering under his eyebrows. "Big fancy word, Mr. Farnon. But ah want the stuff I've allus used."

"Mr. Biggins," said Siegfried in his most reasonable tone. "I wouldn't be a competent veterinary surgeon if I prescribed something so totally outdated." He turned to me. "James, would you slip through to the stockroom and bring a pound packet of the sulfanilamide?"

Mr. Biggins was protesting as I hurried out and was still at it when I returned. Siegfried's smile had faded and I could see that his patience was running out. He seized the packet from me and began to write the instructions on it.

"Three tablespoonfuls in a pint of water daily—"

"But ah tell you ah got no faith in them new things—"

"And after you've used the packet, let us know, and we'll give you more if necessary."

The farmer glared at my partner. "That stuff'll do no good."

"Mr. Biggins," Siegfried said with ominous calm. "It will cure your cow."

"It won't!"

"It will!" Siegfried brought his hand down on the desk with a thud. Clearly he had had enough. "Take this, and if it doesn't do the trick, I won't charge you, all right?"

Something for nothing was irresistible. Mr. Biggins took the sulfanilamide.

"Splendid!" Siegfried jumped up and patted the farmer's shoulder. "Now, get in touch with us when you've used it. I bet you anything your cow will soon be better."

About ten days later Siegfried and I were out on a call together, and on our return we passed Mr. Biggins' farm. "Tell you what, James," my colleague murmured. "Let's drop in. We haven't heard from our friend about the sulfanilamide. Doesn't want to lose face, I suspect." He laughed softly. "We'll be able to rub it in a bit."

He drove around to the back of the house. Outside the kitchen door Siegfried raised his hand to knock, then he stopped and said in an urgent whisper, "Look at that, James!"

He pointed to the kitchen window, and there on the sill was our packet, still unopened. My partner clenched his fist. "The old blighter! He wouldn't even try it—out of sheer spite."

At that moment the farmer opened the door and Siegfried greeted him cheerfully. "Ah, good morning, Mr. Biggins. We were just passing and thought we'd check on your cow." He held up a reassuring hand. "No charge. This is just for our own interest."

"But . . . but . . . I've got me slippers on. Was just havin' a cup o' tea. There's no need for ye to—"

Siegfried was already striding toward the cow byre. The patient was easy to pick out. Her skin was stretched tightly over the jutting ribs, saliva drooled from her lips and a long swelling bulged from under her jaw. Siegfried moved to her quickly, opened the mouth and fingered the tongue.

"Feel that, James," he said softly.

I ran my hand over the knobbly hard surface that gave wooden tongue—or actinobacillosis—its name. "This is awful. It's a wonder she can eat at all." I sniffed at my fingers. "And there's iodine here."

Siegfried nodded. "Yes, he's been to the chemist, despite what I said."

At that moment Mr. Biggins hurried in, panting slightly. My partner looked at him sadly. "Well, you were right. Our medicine hasn't done a bit of good. I can't understand it." He rubbed his chin. "And your poor cow is a mess, I'm afraid. Almost starving to death. I do apologize."

The farmer's face was a study. "Aye, well . . . that's right . . . she's done no good. . . ."

Siegfried broke in. "Look here," he said. "I feel responsible for this. My medicine has failed, so it's up to me to get her right. I have an injection here that ought to do it."

"Now then, wait a minute. . . . I don't know . . ."

But the farmer's words went unheeded as my colleague began to fill a syringe from a bottle I couldn't recognize. With the needle ready for entry he glanced at Mr. Biggins. "It's a good job you've been using our medicine; on its own this injection could have serious effects."

"You mean . . . it could kill 'er?"

"Just possible," Siegfried murmured. "But you've nothing to worry about. She's had the sulfanilamide."

He was about to plunge the needle in when the farmer gave tongue. "Hey, haud on. Don't do that!"

"What is it, Mr. Biggins? Something wrong?"

"Nay, nay, but there's maybe been a bit of a misunderstandin'. Ye see, ah don't think she's been gettin' enough of your stuff."

Siegfried lowered his arm. "You mean you've been underdosing? I wrote the instructions on the packet, if you remember."

"That's right. But ah must have got a bit mixed up."

"No matter. As long as you return her to full dosage, all will be well." Siegfried inserted the needle, ignoring Mr. Biggins' yelp of alarm.

As he put the syringe back in its case, he sighed with satisfaction. "Well, I'm sure that will do the trick. But remember, start

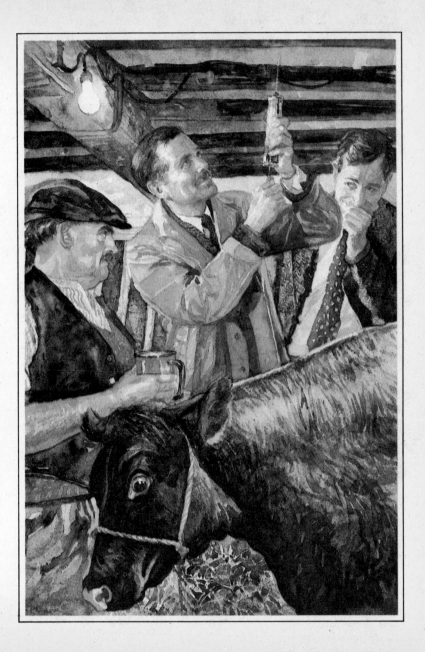

again with the full three tablespoons and continue till you've finished the packet. Let us know if you need a further supply."

As we drove away I stared at my colleague. "What the devil was that injection?"

"Oh, mixed vitamins. It'll help the poor thing's condition, but it had nothing to do with the wooden tongue. Just part of my plan." He smiled gleefully. "Now he's *got* to use the sulfanilamide. It will be interesting to see what happens."

It was indeed interesting. Within a week Mr. Biggins was back in the surgery, looking sheepish.

"Can I have some more o' that stuff?" he muttered.

"By all means." Siegfried extended his arm in an expansive gesture. "As much as you like. I suppose the cow is looking better?"

"Aye."

"Stopped slavering? Putting on flesh, is she?"

"Aye." Mr. Biggins lowered his head as though he didn't want to answer more questions. Siegfried gave him another packet.

When he had left, we watched him through the window. My partner thumped me on the shoulder. "Well, James, that was a little victory. At last we've beaten Mr. Biggins."

The victory was very sweet. Still, when I look back over the years, I realize that that was the only time we did beat him.

8

"This is Amber," Sister Rose said. "The one I wanted you to examine."

I looked at the pale, almost honey-colored hair on the dog's ears and flanks. "I can see why you've given her that name. I bet she'd really glow in the sunshine."

The nurse laughed. "Yes, it was sunny when I first saw her, and the name just jumped into my mind." She gave me a sideways glance. "I'm good at names, you know."

"Oh yes, without a doubt," I said, smiling. It was a little joke between us. Sister Rose had to be good at christening the endless stream of unwanted animals passing through the little dog sanctuary that she maintained behind her house. As a nursing sister she already led a full life of service to the human race. I often asked myself how she found time to fight for the animals, too.

"Where did this one come from?" I asked.

Sister Rose shrugged. "Oh, found wandering in the streets of Hebbleton. Obviously abandoned."

Anger tightened in my throat. "How could anyone do this to such a beautiful dog? Just turn it away to fend for itself."

"People have astonishing reasons. In Amber's case, I think it's because of a little skin disease. Perhaps it frightened them."

"They could at least have taken her to a vet," I grunted as I opened the door of the pen. I noticed some bare patches around the toes, and as I knelt to examine them, Amber nuzzled my cheek and wagged her tail. I looked up at her, at the flopping ears, the pronounced jowls and the trusting eyes that had been betrayed.

"It's a hound's face," I said. "But how about the rest of her? What breed would you call her?"

Sister Rose laughed. "It beats me."

I didn't know either. The body, dappled with patches of brown, black and white, was the wrong shape for a hound. She had very large feet, a long, thin tail in constant motion and everywhere on her coat the delicate sheen of gold.

"Well," I said. "Whatever she is, she's a bonny one, and good-natured, too." I opened the mouth and looked at the rows of untainted teeth. "I'd say she's nine or ten months old—she's just a big pup."

"She'll be really large when she reaches full size."

As if to prove the sister's words, the young bitch reared up and planted her forefeet on my chest. I looked again at the laughing mouth and those eyes. "Amber," I said. "I really like you."

"Oh, I'm so glad," Sister Rose said. "We must get this skin trouble cleared up quickly, so I can find her a home. It's just a bit of eczema, isn't it?"

"Probably . . . probably. . . . I see there's some bareness around the eyes and cheeks, too." Skin diseases in dogs, as in humans, are tricky things, often baffling in origin and difficult to cure. I didn't like the combination here of feet and face, but the skin was dry and sound. Maybe it was nothing much. I banished to the back of my mind a specter that appeared for a brief instant. I didn't want to worry Sister Rose.

"Yes, probably eczema," I said briskly. "Rub in this ointment well twice a day." I handed over a mixture of zinc oxide and lanolin. That, together with the nurse's good feeding, I hoped would do the trick.

When two weeks passed without news of Amber, I was relieved. Then Sister Rose phoned one morning. "Mr. Herriot, those bare patches aren't any better. In fact, they're spreading up her legs and on the face."

The specter leaped up again. "I'll come right out, Sister," I said, and on my way to the car I picked up the microscope.

Amber greeted me as before, with dancing eyes and lashing tail, but I felt sick when I saw the ragged denudation of the face and legs. I got hold of the young animal and held her close, sniffing at the hairless areas.

Sister Rose looked at me in surprise. "What are you doing?"

"Trying to detect a mousy smell. And it's there."

"What does that mean?"

"Mange."

"Oh dear." The nurse put a hand to her mouth. "That's rather nasty, isn't it." Then she put back her shoulders in a characteristic gesture. "Well, I've had experience with mange before, and I can tackle it. I've always been able to clear it up with sulfur baths."

I put Amber down and stood up, feeling suddenly weary. "Yes, but you're thinking of sarcoptic mange, Sister. I'm afraid this is something worse. It looks like demodectic mange." I decided to bite the bullet. "Often incurable."

The specter was very large in my mind now. This disease had haunted me ever since I had qualified, and I had seen many fine dogs put to sleep after prolonged attempts to treat them.

I brought my microscope over from the car. "But I may be jumping the gun. I hope I am. This is the only way to find out."

I squeezed and scraped a patch on Amber's left foreleg with a scalpel blade and prepared a glass slide. Then I looked at it under the microscope and there it was—the dread mite, *Demodex canis.* And there wasn't just one. The whole microscope field was teeming with them.

"There's no doubt about it, Sister," I said. "I'm sorry."

The corners of her mouth drooped. "But . . . isn't there anything we can do?"

"Oh yes, we can try. And we're going to try like anything, because I've taken a fancy to Amber. I've cured a few *Demodex* cases in my time with a lotion." I went to the car and fished around in the trunk. "Here it is—Odylen. Rub it on every day. It may just work."

Sister Rose stuck out her jaw with the determination that had saved so many animals. "I'm sure we can succeed. But how about my other dogs? Won't they become infected?"

I shook my head. "Unlike the sarcoptic mange, demodectic is rarely contagious."

"That's something, anyway. But how on earth does a dog get the disease in the first place?"

"We don't know," I said. "The veterinary profession is pretty well convinced that all dogs have some *Demodex* mites in their skins, but why they should cause mange in some and not in others is unclear. Heredity has something to do with it, because it sometimes occurs in several dogs in the same litter. But it's a baffling business."

I left Sister Rose with the can of Odylen. Maybe this would be one of the exceptions to my experiences with the disease. But within a week I heard from her again. Although she had been applying the Odylen faithfully, the condition was spreading.

I hurried out there. Amber's tail-wagging cheerfulness was undiminished, but her face was disfigured by increasing hairlessness, and when I thought of the beauty that had captivated me on my first visit, the sight was like a blow. I had to try something else, so I started her on a course of Fowler's solution of arsenic, which at that time was popular in treating skin conditions.

When ten days passed I had begun to hope, and it was a bitter disappointment when Sister Rose telephoned just after breakfast, her voice trembling. "Mr. Herriot, she really is deteriorating. Nothing seems to do any good. I'm beginning to think that—"

I cut her off in midsentence. "I'll be there within the hour. Don't give up hope yet. These cases sometimes take months."

I knew as I drove to Sister Rose's sanctuary that my words had no real substance. But I had tried to say something helpful because there was nothing she hated more than putting a dog to sleep. Of all the hundreds of animals she had cared for, I could remember only a handful that had defeated her—very old dogs with chronic kidney or heart conditions, or young ones with distemper. With all the others she had battled until they were fit to go to their new homes. And I myself recoiled from the idea of putting Amber down. Something about that dog had taken hold of me.

When I arrived I still had no idea what I was going to do, so when I spoke, my words rather surprised me. "Sister, I've come to take Amber home with me. You've got enough to do here, looking after your other dogs. I know you've done everything possible, but I'd like to take on this job myself."

"But . . . how will you find the time?"

"I can treat her in the evenings, and this way I'll be able to monitor her progress. I'm determined to get her right."

Driving back to the surgery, I was surprised at the depth of my feeling. Throughout my career I have often had this compulsive desire to cure an animal, but never stronger than with Amber. She was delighted to be in the car with me—she capered around, licking my ear, resting her paws on the dash and peering through the windshield. I looked at her happy face, scarred by the disease, and thumped my hand on the wheel. This was one case that was going to get better.

We had no facilities for boarding dogs—few vets did have at that time—but I made up a comfortable pen for her in the old stable in the yard. Despite its age, the building was free from drafts. She would be snug in there.

I made another decision: to keep Helen out of the whole business. I remembered how stricken she had been when we adopted a cat and then lost him to his rightful owner, and I knew she would soon grow too fond of this dog. But I had forgotten about myself. Veterinary surgeons could never last professionally if they became too involved with their patients. But before I knew what was happening, I became involved with Amber.

I fed her myself, changed her bedding and carried out the treatment. It was late November and darkness came early; after my visits at the farms I always drove around to my yard and trained the headlights on the stable. When I threw open the door, Amber was invariably waiting to welcome me, her forefeet resting on the top of her pen, her long yellow ears gleaming in the bright beam. And her tail swished the straw unceasingly even as I did all the uncomfortable procedures: rubbing the tender skin with lotion, injecting her with staph toxoid and taking further skin scrapings to check progress.

As the days and weeks went by and I saw no improvement, I became a little desperate. I gave her sulfur baths, derris baths and a multitude of shampoos and washes then on the market. I hoped there might be a magic cure among them, despite my misgivings. And I think I might have gone on indefinitely with these nightly sessions under the headlights, if it hadn't been for one very dark evening, when I seemed to see the young dog for the first time. The condition had spread over her entire body. The long ears were golden no longer—they were almost bald, as was the rest of her face and head. Everywhere her skin was thickened and wrinkled and had a bluish tinge.

I flopped back and sat down in the straw while Amber leaped around me, licking and wagging. Despite her terrible state, her nature was unchanged.

But this couldn't go on. I knew now that she and I had come to the end of the road. As I tried to think, I stroked her head, and her cheerful eyes were pathetic in the scarecrow face. What was I going to tell Sister Rose after all my brave words?

It took me until the following noon to summon the will to telephone her. In my effort to be matter-of-fact, I was almost brusque. "Sister," I said, "I'm afraid it's all over with Amber. I've tried everything, and she has got worse. I do think it would be the kindest thing to put her to sleep."

Shock was evident in the good lady's voice. "But . . . it seems so awful. Just for a skin disease."

"I know, but this is a dreadful thing. Amber is very uncomfortable now, and she'll soon be in pain. We can't let her go on."

"Oh . . . well, I trust in your judgment, Mr. Herriot. I know you wouldn't do anything that wasn't necessary." There was a long pause, and I knew she was trying to control her voice. Then she spoke calmly. "Very well. I leave everything to you."

A rush of work kept me going all afternoon, so it was, as always, pitch-dark when I drove into the yard and opened the stable doors. And it was like all the other times. Amber was there in the beam, tail wagging with delight, welcoming me. For a long time I made a fuss over her, patting her and talking to her as she leaped up at me. Then I filled the syringe.

"Sit, girl," I said, and she flopped obediently onto her hindquarters. I gripped her right leg to raise the radial vein, and Amber looked at me with interest, wondering what new game this might be as I slipped in the needle. I realized that there was no need to say the comforting things I always said: "She won't know a thing. . . . This is just an overdose of anesthetic," or "It's an easy way out for her." There was no sorrowing owner to hear me. There were just the two of us.

And as I murmured, "Good girl, Amber, good lass," while she sank down on the straw, I had the conviction that if I had said those comforting things, they would have been true. She *didn't* know a thing between her playfulness and oblivion, and it was indeed an easy way out from her suffering, which soon would have become torture. I stepped from the pen and switched off the car lights, and in the cold darkness the yard had never seemed so empty. After the weeks of struggle, the sense of loss and failure was overpowering.

For a long time I carried a weight around with me, and I feel some of it now after all these years, whenever the picture of her comes into my mind: in the picture it is always dark and Amber is always in the headlight's beam.

Today, demodectic mange can often be cured with organophosphates and antibiotics. Neither was available back when Amber needed them. The tragedy of Amber was that she was born too soon.

9

"Just look at that," the farmer said.

"At what?" I was "cleansing" a cow—removing the afterbirth—and my arm was buried deep in the cow's uterus. I turned my head to see him pointing at the animal's udder. Four white jets of milk were spurting out of it onto the floor.

He grinned. "That's a funny thing, isn't it?"

"Not really," I said. "It's a reflex action from the brain caused by my hand twiddling the uterus about. I often see cows letting their milk down like that when I'm cleansing them."

"Well, that's a rum un." The farmer laughed. "Any road, you'd better get finished quick or you'll have a few pints of milk to knock off your bill."

That was in 1947, the year of the great snow. I have never known snow like that before or since. After Christmas it began to get colder and colder. All through January a northeast wind blew; then, borne on the wind, very fine flakes appeared and by February big fat flakes—a steady, relentless descent that went on for weeks, sometimes falling in a lazy curtain that remorselessly obliterated the familiar landmarks, at other times in fierce blizzards. In between, the frost took over and transformed the roads into glassy tracks of flattened snow.

To get to our cases we did a lot of walking, since so many of the farm tracks were blocked. On the very high country there were some farms we couldn't reach at all, and many animals undoubtedly died for lack of veterinary help. It was around mid-March, when helicopters were dropping food on these isolated spots, that Bert Kealey—who ran a small herd of cattle on the high tops of the moors—telephoned me.

"I thought your phone wires would be down, Bert," I said.

"Naw, they've survived. I don't know how." The young man's voice was cheerful, as always. "But ah'm in trouble," he went on. "Polly's just had a litter, and she hasn't a drop of milk."

"Oh, dear, that's unfortunate," I said. Polly was the only pig on the Kealey farm.

"Aye. Bad enough losin' the litter—twelve smashin' little pigs—but it's Tess I'm bothered about."

"Yes . . . yes. . . ." I was thinking of Tess, too. She was Bert's eight-year-old daughter, and she had a thing about little pigs. She had persuaded her father to buy her an in-pig sow for her birthday so that she could have a litter of her own. I could remember Tess's excitement when she had shown me the pig.

"That's Polly," she said, pointing to the sow nuzzling the straw in its pen. "She's mine. My dad gave her to me."

I leaned over the pen. "Yes, I know. You're a lucky girl. She looks a fine pig."

"Oh, she is." The little girl's eyes shone with pleasure. "I feed her every day, and she lets me stroke her. And do you know something else?" Tess's voice took on a conspiratorial tone. "She's going to have babies in March."

"Well, I never!" I said. "Is that so? You'll have a whole lot of little pink pigs to look after." I held my hands a few inches apart. "Just about this size."

She was so thrilled at the thought, she was lost for words.

Now all this came back to me as I listened to Bert Kealey's voice on the phone.

"Do you think Polly's got mastitis, Bert?" I asked him. "Is the udder red and swollen? Is she off her food?"

"No, nowt like that. She's eatin' her head off, and her udder's not a bit inflamed."

"Well, then, it's a straight case of agalactia. She needs a shot of pituitrin to bring down the milk, but how is she going to get it? Your district's been cut off for weeks."

It takes a lot to make a Yorkshire farmer admit that his farm is inaccessible because of the weather, but in these exceptional circumstances, Bert had to agree. "I know," he said. "Ah've tried diggin' me road out, but it fills up as fast as I clear it. Anyway, top road's blocked for two miles, so I'm wastin' me time."

I thought for a moment. "Have you tried getting some cow's milk into the piglets? An egg mixed with a quart of milk and a teaspoonful of glucose isn't a bad substitute."

"I've tried that, but they wouldn't look at it," Bert replied. "If only they could have a good suck at their mother to start them off, then maybe they'd have a go at t'substitute."

He was right. There was nothing to compare with that first suck. And without it, those tiny creatures would soon die.

I tapped my fingers against the receiver. An idea was forming in my mind. "Look, Bert," I said. "I know I can get to the top of Dennor Bank, because the road is open to there. After that it's all flat going to your place. Maybe I could get there on skis."

"Skis?"

"Yes, I've been doing a bit of that lately. But I've not tackled anywhere as far off as your farm. I can't be sure I'll make it, but I'll try."

"By 'eck, I'd be grateful, Mr. Herriot. It's t'little lass ah'm thinkin' of."

"Same here, Bert. Anyway, I'll have a go. I'm leaving now."

On the summit of Dennor Bank, I maneuvered my car as close as possible to the tall white walls the snowplows had thrown up; then I got out and buckled on my skis. I have to admit I was beginning to fancy myself on skis, because one bonus of the long spell of snow was that some nice slopes had become available. With a few other enthusiasts I had found that gliding down the hillsides was most exhilarating. I had even bought a book on the subject and thought I was becoming quite skillful.

All I needed was the bottle of pituitrin and a syringe, and I put them in my pocket.

Normally to get to the Kealey farm you drove a couple of miles along a straight road, turned right and made for the high-lying village of Branderley. Bert's farm lay in an isolated position about halfway between that turn and the village.

But that day, although I had traveled the region a hundred times, I might have been in a strange country; the stone walls had been deeply engulfed, so there were no fields, no roads, nothing but a yawning white expanse with the tops of telegraph poles sticking up here and there. It was uncanny. I felt a twinge of misgiving, but at least I could travel cross-country. It would be like cutting off two sides of a triangle, and I was pretty sure the farm lay in one of the hollows just below the dark skyline.

I had slithered amateurishly for about half a mile when the snow started again. A dense white veil obliterated my sense of direction. There is no disguising the fact that I was scared. I stood stock-still in the cold with my eyes half closed, wondering what would happen to me. I could blunder for miles in that empty wilderness without coming upon a house.

Then, just as suddenly as it had begun, the flurry stopped. My heart thumped as I stared around me, and the dark smudge of my car roof in the white distance was a sweet sight. I headed back to it with a speed worthy of an Olympic skier. Upon reaching my link with home, I started the engine and I was well on the way to Darrowby before my pulse rate returned to normal.

"Bert," I said on the phone when I returned. "I'm terribly sorry, but I got caught by a snow shower and had to turn back."

"Well, ah'm glad ye did turn back. I've been a bit worried since ye left. Fellers have got lost and died in the snow up here. I shouldn't have let you try." He paused for a moment, then said wistfully, "If only there was some other way to make Polly let 'er milk down."

As he spoke, the picture flashed into my mind of that cow I was cleansing and the jets of milk striking the byre floor. And there were other memories—when I'd done uterine examinations on sows, the same thing had happened.

"Maybe there is a way," I blurted out. "Have you ever had your hand inside a sow? Examined one internally?"

"In 'er pig bed? Nay, ah leave that to you chaps."

"Well, I want you to start now. Get some warm water and—"

"Hey, hang on, Mr. Herriot. I'm sure there's no more pigs left in 'er."

"I don't suppose there are, Bert, but do as I say. Soap your arm well and use any household antiseptic you have. Then put your hand inside the pig and waggle the uterus around a bit."

"Oh, 'eck, I don't fancy this. What's it all about?"

"It often brings the milk down. So get going."

I hung up and went in to have lunch. While I was eating, the phone rang. It was Bert, breathless but triumphant. "It worked, Mr. Herriot! I 'ad a waggle round like you said, then I tried the udder. I could draw milk out of every tit. It was like magic."

"Are the piglets feeding?"

"Aye, it's lovely to see them."

"Well, that's great," I said. "But we haven't won yet. Polly will probably dry up again by tomorrow. You'll have to get your hand in again."

"Oh, crumbs." A lot of the enthusiasm went out of Bert's voice. "I thought I'd finished wi' that."

The poor man did indeed have to perform his unusual task several times, and Polly never did come fully to her milk, but the piglets were kept going until they were able to drink the milk substitute. The litter was saved.

In late April in the high country the white streaks still lay behind the walls, standing out against the green moorland like the ribs of a great beast. But the roads were clear, and I went to see one of Bert Kealey's heifers. When I had finished my job, young Tess took me to see her beloved Polly and family.

"They're pretty, aren't they?" she said as we watched the twelve chunky little pigs playing around their mother.

"They certainly are, Tess," I replied. "Your first attempt at pig breeding has been a big success, and you have your father to thank for the job he did."

Bert gave a wry smile, then screwed up his face at the memory. "Aye, maybe so, and I reckon it was worth it. It's wonderful what ye can do when you have to."

10

"ARE you all right, Helen?"

I looked around anxiously as my wife fidgeted in her seat. We were in La Scala cinema in Brawton, and I had a strong conviction that we had no right to be there.

I had voiced my doubts that morning. "I know it's our half day, Helen, but with the baby due anytime, don't you think it would be safer to stay around Darrowby?"

"No, of course not." Helen had laughed incredulously at the idea of missing our outing, an oasis of relaxation for both of us. For me it was an escape from the telephone and the mud and the Wellington boots, and for my wife it was a rest from her own hard slog, plus the luxury of having meals cooked and served by somebody else.

"It's all right you laughing," I had said. "But what if it comes on quickly? Do we want our second child born in Smith's bookshop or the back of a car?"

There is never much of the yogi in my makeup, but now I just couldn't be calm about this thing. The whole business had me worried. People make jokes about this syndrome, but I didn't find it funny. Something about having babies really got to me, and lately I had spent a lot of time flapping around watching Helen's every move, much to her amusement. Over the last two days the tension had really built up.

This morning Helen had been adamant: she wasn't going to be done out of her half day. And now here we were in La Scala, with Humphrey Bogart competing vainly for my attention while my wife squirmed and from time to time ran a thoughtful hand over her swollen abdomen.

Now, as I scrutinized her keenly from the corner of my eye, she gave a convulsive jerk and a soft moan. Perspiration had already sprung out all over me before she whispered, "I think we'd better go, Jim."

Stumbling over the outstretched legs in the darkness, I guided her up the sloping aisle, past the usherette, to the street and our car. The twenty-five miles to Darrowby seemed to take an eternity, and the rattles and the bumping springs made me wish, for the only time in my life, that I had a Rolls-Royce. Helen sat quietly by my side, occasionally closing her eyes and catching her breath, while my heart beat a tattoo against my ribs. When we reached our town I turned toward the marketplace.

Helen looked at me in surprise. "Where are you going?"

"Well, to Nurse Brown's, of course."

"Oh, don't be so silly. It's not time for that yet."

"But . . . how do you know?"

"I've had a baby before, remember? Come on, let's go home."

Heavy with misgiving, I drove to Skeldale House, and as we mounted the stairs I marveled at Helen's composure. It was the same when we got into bed. She lay there, obviously not comfortable but with a calm acceptance of the inevitable.

I suppose I kept dropping into what is termed a fitful slumber, because it was six a.m. when she nudged my arm.

"Time to go, Jim." Her tone was matter-of-fact.

I shot from the bed like a jack-in-the-box, threw on my clothes and shouted across the landing to Auntie Lucy, who was staying with us for the occasion. "We're off!"

A faint reply came through the door. "All right. I'll see to Jimmy."

Outside, it was a glorious May morning, the air limpid with the new-day freshness that had soothed the irritation of many an early call, but it was all lost on me as I drove to the small dwelling of Nurse Brown. Upstairs there were a couple of bedrooms that for many years had seen the arrival of the local children.

I knocked at the door and pushed it open. Nurse Brown gave me a quick smile and led Helen upstairs. I was left in the kitchen, feeling helpless, when a voice cut in on my jumbled thoughts. "Now then, Jim, it's a grand mornin'."

It was Cliff, Nurse Brown's husband. He was sitting in the corner eating breakfast, his face wreathed in its usual broad grin. I suppose I half expected him to leap up, seize my hand and say, "There, there," or something of the sort. However, he continued to work his way phlegmatically through the stack of bacon, eggs, sausages and tomatoes on his plate, and I realized that over the years he must have seen hundreds of quivering husbands standing in that kitchen. It was old stuff to Cliff.

"Yes, Cliff . . . yes. . . ." I replied. "I think it will turn out hot later." I cringed inwardly at the creaking sounds from the floorboards above. What was happening in that bedroom?

Cliff pushed his plate to one side before turning his attention to bread and marmalade. As he chewed, he seemed to notice that I was perhaps one of the more distraught husbands, because he turned his big, kind smile on me.

"Don't worry, lad," he said gently. "It'll be right."

His words were mildly soothing, and I fled. In those days it was unheard-of for the husband to be present at the birth, and though it is now the "in" thing for the men to observe it all, I marvel at their fortitude; I know beyond all doubt that Herriot would be carried away unconscious from such proceedings.

When Siegfried arrived at Skeldale House, he was thoughtful. "You'd better stick around, James. I'll do the morning rounds on my own. Take it quietly, my boy. All will be well."

It was difficult to take it quietly. I found that expectant fathers really did pace the floor, and I varied this by trying to read the newspaper upside down.

It was around eleven o'clock when the long-awaited telephone call came from my doctor and good friend, Harry Allinson. Harry always spoke in a sort of cheerful shout, and this morning his booming voice was like the sweetest music. "A sister for Jimmy!"

"Oh, great, Harry. Thank you. That's marvelous news." I held the receiver against my chest for a few moments before putting it down. I walked with dragging steps to the sitting room and lay back in a chair until my nerves had stopped vibrating.

Then, on an impulse, I leaped to my feet. Normally I am fairly sensible, but I decided that I had to go to Nurse Brown's immediately. I knew that a husband was not welcome straight after the birth, because I had gone to see Jimmy too soon and had not been well received. But still I went.

When I burst into her establishment, Nurse Brown's usual smile was absent. "You've done it again," she said with some asperity. "I told you with Jimmy that you should have given us time to get the baby washed, but it seems you took no notice."

I hung my head sheepishly, and she relented. "Oh well, now you're here you might as well come upstairs."

Helen had the same tired, flushed look that I remembered from before. I kissed her thankfully. We didn't say anything, just smiled at each other. Then I had a look in the cot by the bed. Last time I had been so aghast at Jimmy's appearance that I had mortally offended Nurse Brown by asking if there was anything wrong with him, and heaven help me, I felt the same way now. My new little daughter's face was red and bloated, and the sense of shock hit me as it had done before.

I looked up at the nurse, whose scowling face made it only too clear that she was waiting for me to say something derogatory.

"Gorgeous," I said weakly. "Really gorgeous."

"All right." She had seen enough of me. "Out you go." She ushered me downstairs, and as she opened the outside door, she fixed me with a piercing eye, speaking slowly and deliberately, as though addressing a person of limited intelligence. "That . . . is . . . a . . . lovely . . . healthy . . . baby." She then closed the door in my face.

And, bless her heart, her words helped me; as I drove away, I knew she must be right.

When I returned to Skeldale House, there was one visit waiting for me, high in the hills, and the journey there was like a happy dream. My worry was over, and it seemed that all nature was rejoicing with me. It was the ninth of May, 1947, the prelude to the most perfect summer I can remember. The sun blazed and soft breezes swirled into the car, carrying their fragrance from the fells: an elusive breath of bluebells, primroses and violets scattered everywhere on the grass.

After I had seen my patient, I took a walk on the high tops, along a favorite path on the hill's edge, with Sam trotting at my heels. I looked away over the rolling patchwork of the plain, sleeping in the sun's haze, and at the young bracken on the hillside, springing straight and green from last year's dead brown stalks. Everywhere new life was calling out its exultant message—

and, for me, aptly so, with my new little daughter down there in Darrowby.

We had decided to call her Rosemary. It is such a pretty name and I still love it, but it became Rosie at a very early stage, and though I did make one or two ineffectual stands, it has remained so to this day.

I would have liked to continue reclining in the sunshine on the springy bed of heather that clusters on these hillsides. But on that May day I had other things to do. I sped back to Skeldale House and began to telephone my glad news all over the country. It was received rapturously by all, but it was Tristan who grasped the essentials of the situation.

"We've got to wet this baby's head, Jim," he said seriously. "I'll be over at seven."

And at seven o'clock there were four of us in the sitting room at Skeldale House—Siegfried, Tristan, Alex Taylor and myself. Alex was my oldest friend—we had started school together in Glasgow at the age of four. It was good that he should be with me tonight.

Tristan was concerned about the venue of the celebration. His fingers drummed on the arm of his chair as he thought aloud, and his expression was fixed and grave. "Let's see, now," he muttered. "We'd normally go to the Drovers, but they've got that big party on tonight. We could go to the George and Dragon for Tetley's beer—splendid stuff, but I've known them a bit careless with their pipes and I've had the odd sour mouthful. And of course we have the Cross Keys. They pull a lovely pint of Cameron's, and the draft Guinness is excellent. And we mustn't forget the Hare and Pheasant—"

"Just a minute, Triss," I broke in. "I went to Nurse Brown's this evening to see Helen, and Cliff asked if he could come with us. Don't you think it would be rather nice to go to his regular pub, since the baby was born in his house?"

Tristan narrowed his eyes. "Which pub is that?"

"The Black Horse."

"Ah yes, ye-es." Tristan looked at me thoughtfully and put his fingertips together. "I've had some first-rate Russell and

Rangham's there, though I've noticed a slight loss of nuttiness under very warm conditions." He looked anxiously out the window. "It's been a hot day today. Perhaps we'd—"

"Oh, for heaven's sake!" Siegfried leaped to his feet. "It's only beer you're talking about; you sound like an analytical chemist! I think the Black Horse is a pleasant idea, James. It's a quiet little place."

And indeed, when we arrived I felt we had chosen the ideal spot. The evening sunshine sent long golden shafts over the pitted oak tables and the high-backed settles, where a few farm men sat with their glasses. There was nothing smart about this little inn, but the furniture, which hadn't been changed for a hundred years, gave it an air of tranquillity.

Reg Wilkey, the diminutive landlord, welcomed us and charged our glasses from his tall white jug, and Siegfried raised his pint. "James, may I be the first to wish a long life, health and happiness to Rosemary."

"Thank you, Siegfried," I said, feeling suddenly very much among friends as the others said, "Hear, hear," and began to drink.

After a few pints, Siegfried patted me on the shoulder. "I'm off, James. Have a good time. Can't tell you how pleased I am."

I watched him go, and I didn't argue. He was right. There was a veterinary practice out there, and somebody had to watch the shop. And this was my night.

It was one of those cozy evenings when everything seemed perfect. Alex and I recalled our childhood in Glasgow, Tristan came up with some splendid memories of Skeldale House in the bachelor days, and over everything, like a beneficent moon, hung the huge smile of Cliff Brown. When Reg Wilkey was obliged by law to announce closing time, we simply adjourned to the pub's cellar, where we stayed, talking and enjoying ourselves, until well after midnight. Then, warmed by the day's events, my anxieties behind me, I went home full of a great love of my fellowmen.

In Skeldale House, I walked up to our big bedroom; it seemed eerily empty without Helen. I opened the door to the long, narrow room that had been the dressing room in the great days of the old house. It was where Tristan had slept when we were all bachelors together, but now it was Jimmy's room, and his bed stood in exactly the same place as had my old friend's.

I looked down on my sleeping son, then glanced at the other end of the room, where a cot stood to receive Rosie. Soon, I thought, I would have two in here. I was becoming rich.

11

I WINCED as the farmer's slender frame was thrown against the cow's ribs, but Jack Scott himself didn't seem troubled. He took a fresh grip on the tail and braced himself for further action.

I was trying to treat the cow for infertility—but it involved the insertion of a long metal catheter through the uterine cervix, and this animal didn't seem to appreciate it. Every time I attempted to work the catheter in, she swung around violently and the farmer was whirled against the neighboring cow.

But this time I had the feeling I was winning. The tube was sliding in nicely. If only she would stand still for a few seconds, the job would be over. "Hang on, Jack," I gasped as I began to pump Lugol's iodine into the catheter. As soon as the cow felt the fluid trickling in, she veered over again and the farmer was squashed once more between the big creatures. I withdrew the catheter and stepped back, thinking that this had been a singularly uncooperative patient.

Jack, however, didn't seem to share my view. He went up to the front of the cow and put his arms around her neck. "Ah, you're a grand lass," he murmured. It was always like this with Jack. He had a deep affection for every creature on his farm, and the feeling always seemed to be returned.

When he had concluded his embrace, he pushed his way out, smiling as usual. Jack did not have the ruddy hue of the typical farmer. His face was pale and haggard, with deep wrinkles that made him look older than his forty years. But his smile was radiant, like an inner light.

"Ah've another job for ye, Mr. Herriot," he said. "There's some lambs ah want ye to look at. I've never seen owt like them."

We walked across the yard with Jack's sheep dog, Rip, gamboling around his master in delight. Often these farm dogs were slinking, furtive creatures, but Rip behaved like a happy pet. The farmer bent and patted him. "Hello, feller, are you comin', too?"

He led me into a Nissen hut, where there were a number of ewes and lambs. Several of the lambs were wobbling on their hind legs as they walked, and two could take only a few faltering steps before collapsing.

Jack turned to me. "What's the matter wi' them, Mr. Herriot?"

"They've got swayback," I replied. "It's caused by a copper deficiency that results in degeneration of the brain. Typically it makes them weak in their hindquarters, but sometimes they become paralyzed or take fits."

"That's strange," the farmer said. "Them ewes have had copper licks to go at all the time."

"I'm afraid that's not enough. If you get many cases, you ought to inject the ewes with copper halfway through pregnancy to prevent it next time."

He sighed. "Ah well, now we know what it is, you'll be able to put these lambs right."

"Sorry, Jack. The ones that are just wobbly have a good chance of making it, but I haven't much hope for those two." I pointed to the pair lying on their sides. "They're already partially paralyzed. I honestly think the kindest thing would be . . ."

That was when the smile left Jack's face. It always did at the merest suggestion of putting an animal down. It is a country vet's duty to advise his clients when treatment is unprofitable; he must always have the farmer's commercial interest in mind. But this system didn't work with Jack. He had animals on the farm that could not possibly be making him money, but they were his friends and he was happy to see them pottering about.

He dug his hands deep in his pockets and looked down at the prostrate lambs. "Are they sufferin', Mr. Herriot?"

"No, Jack, no. It doesn't seem to be a painful disease."

"Awright, I'll keep 'em. If they can't suck, I'll feed 'em meself. Ah like to give things a chance."

As the summer wore on, I was glad to see that his dedication had paid off. The two semiparalyzed lambs were surviving and doing well. They still flopped down after a few steps, but they were able to nibble the fast-growing grass, and the brain degeneration mercifully had not progressed.

It was in October, when the trees were a blaze of color, that Jack hailed me as I drove past his gate. "Will ye stop and see Rip?" His face was anxious.

"Why, is he ill?"

"Naw, naw, just lame, but I can't mek it out."

The dog was, as ever, close to his master; I saw that his right foreleg was trailing uselessly.

"What's happened to him?" I asked.

"He was roundin' up t'cows when one of 'em lashed out and got him on the chest. He's been gettin' lamer ever since. The funny thing is, ah can't find a thing wrong with his leg."

Rip wagged vigorously as I examined him. There was no pain in the limb, no wound or injury, but he winced as I passed my hand over his first rib. Diagnosis was not difficult.

"It's radial paralysis," I said.

"Radial . . . What's that?"

"The radial nerve passes over the first rib, and the kick must have damaged rib and nerve. This has put the extensor muscles out of action so that he can't bring his leg forward."

"Well, that's a rum un." The farmer passed a hand over the shaggy head. "Will he get better?"

"It's usually a long job—weeks or months. Nervous tissue is slow to regenerate, and treatment doesn't seem to help much."

The farmer nodded. "Awright, we'll just have to wait. One thing"—and again the bright smile flooded his face—"he can still round up the cows, lame or not. It 'ud break 'is heart if he couldn't work. Loves 'is job, does Rip."

On the way to the car I tried to say something encouraging. "Don't worry too much, Jack. These cases usually recover in time."

But Rip did not recover. After several months his leg was as useless as ever, and the muscles had wasted greatly. The nerve must have been damaged irreparably, and it was an unhappy thought that this attractive little animal was going to be three-legged for the rest of his life.

Jack was undismayed and maintained stoutly that Rip was still a good working dog.

The real blow fell one Sunday morning as Siegfried and I were arranging the rounds in the office. I answered the doorbell and found Jack carrying his dog. "What's wrong?" I asked. "Is he worse?"

"No, Mr. Herriot." The farmer's voice was husky. "It's summat different. He's been knocked down."

Siegfried and I examined the dog on the surgery table. "Fracture of the tibia," my partner said. "But there's no sign of internal damage. Do you know exactly what happened?"

Jack nodded. "He ran onto the street and a car caught 'im. He dragged 'imself back into t'yard."

"Dragged?" Siegfried was puzzled.

"Aye, the broken leg's on the same side as t'other thing."

My partner blew out his cheeks. "Ah yes, the radial paralysis. I remember you told me about it, James." He looked at me and I knew we were thinking the same thing: a fracture and a paralysis on the same side were a forbidding combination.

We did what we could—we set the leg in plaster. As he was leaving, Jack smiled. "I'm takin' the family to church this mornin', and I'll say a prayer for Rip while I'm there."

Afterward Siegfried was thoughtful. "I just hope that job goes right," he said. "Jack's a truly remarkable chap. He says he's going to pray for his dog and there's nobody better qualified. Remember what Coleridge said? *He prayeth best, who loveth best/All things both great and small.*"

"Yes," I said. "That's Jack, all right."

The farmer brought his dog into the surgery six weeks later for the removal of the plaster. I sawed it off, palpated the limb, and my spirits plummeted. Hardly any healing had taken place. There should have been a healthy callus by now, but I could feel the loose ends of the broken bones moving against each other, almost like a hinge. Siegfried was in the dispensary, and I called to him.

He felt the leg. "Drat!" He looked at the farmer. "We'll have to try again, Jack, but I don't like it."

We applied a fresh plaster, and the farmer grinned confidently. "Just wanted more time, I reckon. He'll be right next time."

But it was not to be. Siegfried and I stripped off the second cast together, but the situation was unchanged. There was little or no healing tissue around the fracture.

"It's just the same, I'm afraid, Jack," I told the farmer.

"You mean it 'asn't joined up?"

"That's right."

Jack rubbed a finger along his upper lip. "Then 'e won't be able to take any weight on that leg?"

"I don't see how."

"Aye . . . well, we'll just have to see how he goes on."

"But, Jack," Siegfried said gently. "Two useless legs on the same side? He can't go on."

I could see the familiar curtain coming down over the farmer's face. He knew what was in our minds, and he wasn't going to have it. I knew what he was going to say next.

"Is he sufferin'?"

"No, he isn't," Siegfried replied. "There's no pain in the fracture now and the paralysis is painless anyway, but he won't be able to walk, don't you see?"

Jack was already gathering his dog in his arms. "We'll give him a chance, any road," he said.

When he had left, Siegfried looked at me wide-eyed. "What do you make of that, James?"

"Same as you," I replied gloomily. "Poor old Jack. He always gives everything a chance, but he's got no hope this time."

But I was wrong. Several weeks later I was called to the Scott farm to look at a sick calf, and the first thing I saw was Rip bringing the cows in for milking. He was darting to and fro around the rear of the herd, guiding them through the gate from the field, and I watched him in amazement. He still could not bear any appreciable weight on his right limbs, yet he was running happily, somehow supporting his body with his two strong left legs and the paws of the stricken limbs merely brushing the turf. Jack didn't say anything about "I told you so," and I wouldn't have cared if he had, because it thrilled me to see the little animal doing the job he loved.

"This calf, Mr. Herriot." The farmer dragged me back to the matter at hand. "Never seen one like it. Goin' round and round as if it was daft."

Depression flowed over me. I had been hoping for something straightforward this time. My recent contacts with Jack's animals could be described as abortive treatment and wrong prognosis, and I did want to pull something out of the bag. This didn't sound good.

It was a bonny little calf about a month old. Dark roan—the Shorthorn farmer's favorite color—and it was lying on its straw bed looking fairly normal, except that its head was inclined slightly to one side. Jack touched the rump with his toe, and the calf rose to its feet.

That was where the normality ended, because the little creature blundered helplessly to the right, as if drawn by a magnet, until it walked into the wall. It picked itself up and recommenced its progress, always to the right.

So that was it. I took the animal's temperature. It was 106 degrees. "This is called listeriosis, Jack," I said. "Circling disease is another name for it, and you can see why. It affects the brain."

The farmer looked glum. "Brain again, just like them lambs? There must be summat in the air about here." He paused, bent over the calf and began to stroke it. "And there'll be nowt you can do for this either, I suppose."

"I hope I can do something, Jack. This is different from the lambs. It's an actual bug affecting the brain, and with a bit of luck I can put this calf right."

I felt like crossing my fingers. In the prewar days these cases had been fatal, but the causal organism was sensitive to antibiotics and now the whole scene had changed. I had seen animals with listeriosis recover completely within a few days.

I injected the calf with a penicillin-streptomycin suspension, a recent acquisition in our profession. Then I turned to Jack.

"I'll be back tomorrow," I said. "I hope to find some improvement by then."

Next day the temperature was down, but the symptoms had not abated. I repeated the injection and said I would call again.

I did call, again and again; but after a week, though the temperature was normal and the appetite excellent, the calf was still circling.

"How d'you feel about t'job, Mr. Herriot?" the farmer asked.

Actually I felt like screaming. Was there a hoodoo on this place? I calmed down and took a deep breath. "I'm sorry, Jack, but we don't seem to be getting anywhere. The antibiotic has saved the calf's life, but there must be some brain damage. I can't see any hope of recovery now."

He didn't seem to have heard me. "It's a grand un, a heifer, too, and out of me best cow. She'll make a smashin' milker—and just look at that color. We've called her Bramble."

"Yes. But, Jack . . ."

He patted me on the shoulder and led me out to the yard. "Well, thank ye, Mr. Herriot. Ah'm sure you've done all you can." Clearly he didn't want to pursue the matter further. He had decided to give Bramble a chance.

IT TURNED out that Jack's faith was rewarded and that my prognosis was wrong again, but I could not blame myself this time, because the sequence of events in Bramble's recovery was not contained in any textbook.

Over the next two years the brain symptoms gradually diminished. The improvement was so slow as to be almost imperceptible, but every time I was on Jack's farm I looked in on her and saw to my astonishment that the animal was a bit better. For many weeks she circled, then this subsided into an occasional staggering toward the right. This in turn faded into an inclination of the head to one side, until one day this, too, disappeared and a fine normal heifer was strolling around. I was delighted.

"Jack," I said. "How marvelous! I'd have bet anything that this was a hopeless case, and there she is, absolutely perfect."

The farmer gave me a slow smile with a hint of mischief in it.

"Aye, ah'm right capped with her, Mr. Herriot, and she's goin' to be one of the best cows in the herd before she's finished. But"—he raised a finger and his smile broadened—"she's not perfect. There's just a little somethin'." He leaned toward me conspiratorially. "Keep watchin' her face."

I stared at the heifer, mystified. "I can't see a— What!"

The farmer laughed. "Did ye see it?"

I certainly had, and it was startling. Just for an instant Bramble's placid expression was transfigured by a faint twitch of the eyes and head to the right. There was something human about the gesture, a come-hither look reminiscent of the film vamps of the 1920s.

Jack was still laughing. "I reckon you've never seen owt like that afore, Mr. Herriot?"

"No, I haven't. Quite extraordinary! How often does she do it?"

"Oh, every now and then. I suppose it'll go away in time like all t'other things?"

"I expect it will," I said. "But how very strange."

"Aye." Jack nodded. "Well, I'm glad we persevered with 'er." (It was nice of him to say we.) "Ah've had 'er served, and she should be calvin' just right for Darrowby show."

"Well, that will be interesting. She's certainly a picture."

It was true. Bramble had developed into a classic Dairy Shorthorn with all the delicacy and grace of that now lost breed—the beautifully straight back, the neat tailhead and the makings of a fine udder.

She was even more of a picture a few months later as she stood in the center of the show-ring with the August sun glinting on her rich dark coat. She had recently produced a calf, and her udder, tight and flat-based, bulged between the back limbs. Surpassing her would take some doing, and it was a pleasant thought that the seemingly doomed creature of two and a half years ago might be just about to win a championship trophy.

However, Bramble was in pretty hot company. The judge, Brigadier Rowan, had narrowed the field down to three, and the other two contestants, a red-and-white and a light roan, were beautiful animals. It was going to be close.

Brigadier Rowan was a distinguished soldier, a gentleman farmer and an unrivaled judge of dairy cattle in the district, and his dress and bearing were fully in keeping with his position. That tall lean figure would have been impressive even without the beautifully cut suit, waistcoat and bowler hat. The fact that he was wearing a monocle added the final touch.

The brigadier strolled down the little row of cattle, occasionally screwing the glass tighter into his eye as he bent to inspect a particular point. Clearly he was having difficulty deciding. His normally pink face was bright red, not, I felt, from the sunshine but from the long succession of whiskies and soda I had seen him consuming in the judge's tent. Finally he pursed his lips and approached Bramble. He leaned forward and peered into the animal's face as though to examine the eyes. Something happened then. I could not see Bramble's face, but my suspicion is that she gave the little twitch that had startled me, because the brigadier's eyebrows shot up and the monocle dropped to the end of its cord, where it dangled for a few seconds before he returned it to his eye.

He studied Bramble fixedly for quite a long time, and even after he had moved away he glanced back at her once or twice. I could read his mind. Had he really seen that, or was it the whisky?

He came slowly back down the row. He had the look of a man who was definitely going to make up his mind. He finished up once more in front of Bramble. As he gave her a final appraising stare he flinched, and I had a strong conviction that she had done her trick again.

The monocle remained in position this time, but the brigadier was obviously shaken. The experience, however, seemed to remove all doubt from his mind; he immediately placed Bramble first. The poor man really had no option.

Later, when he strode to the edge of the ring, he was greeted by a beaming Jack. "A bonny lass, 'ant she, Brigadier? Almost human, ye might say."

"Quite," said the brigadier, adjusting his monocle. "Actually, she reminds me of someone I used to know."

12

In the semidarkness of the surgery passage I thought it was a hideous growth dangling from the side of the dog's face, but as he came closer I saw that it was only a condensed-milk can. I was relieved because I knew I was dealing with Brandy again.

I hoisted him onto the table. "Brandy, you've been at the dustbin again." The big golden Labrador gave me an apologetic grin and did his best to lick my face. He couldn't manage it, since his tongue was jammed under the lid, but he made up for it by a furious wagging of his tail.

"Oh, Mr. Herriot, I am sorry to trouble you again." Mrs. Westby, his attractive young mistress, smiled ruefully. "He just won't keep out of that dustbin. Sometimes the children and I can get the cans off by ourselves, but this one is stuck fast."

I eased my finger along the jagged edge of the metal. "It's a bit tricky, isn't it? We don't want to cut him."

As I reached for the forceps, I thought of the many other occasions when I had done something like this for Brandy. He was a huge, lolloping, slightly goofy animal, and this dustbin raiding was becoming an obsession. He liked to fish out a can and lick up the tasty remnants, with such dedication that he often got stuck. Time after time he had been freed by his family or myself from fruit-salad cans, corned-beef cans, baked-bean cans, soup cans—there didn't seem to be anything he didn't like.

I gripped the edge of the lid with my forceps and gently bent it back along its length till I was able to lift it away from the tongue. An instant later that tongue was slobbering all over my cheek as Brandy expressed his delight and thanks.

"Get back, you daft dog!" I said, laughing.

"Yes, come down, Brandy." Mrs. Westby hauled him from the table and spoke sharply. "It's fine making a fuss now, but you're becoming a nuisance with this business. It will have to stop."

The scolding had no effect on the lashing tail, and I saw that his mistress was smiling. You just couldn't help liking Brandy, because he was a great ball of affection and tolerance, without an ounce of malice in him. I had seen the Westby children—three girls and a boy—carrying him around upside down, or pushing him in a pram, dressed in baby clothes. Those youngsters played all sorts of games with him, but he suffered them all with good humor. In fact, I am sure he enjoyed them.

Brandy had other idiosyncrasies, apart from his fondness for dustbins. I was attending the Westby cat at their home one afternoon when I saw the dog acting strangely. Mrs. Westby was knitting in an armchair, while the oldest girl squatted on the hearthrug with me and held the cat's head.

It was when I was searching my pockets for my thermometer that I noticed Brandy slinking into the room. He wore a furtive air as he moved across the carpet and sat down with studied carelessness in front of his mistress. After a few moments he began to work his rear gradually up the front of the chair toward her knees. Absently she pushed him down, but he immediately restarted his backward ascent, his hips moving in a slow rumba rhythm as he elevated them inch by inch, and all the time the golden face was blank and innocent, as though nothing at all were happening.

Fascinated, I stopped hunting for my thermometer and watched. Mrs. Westby was absorbed in her knitting and didn't seem to notice that Brandy's bottom was now firmly parked on her shapely knees, which were clad in blue jeans. The dog paused, as though acknowledging that phase one had been successfully completed; then ever so gently he began to consolidate his position, pushing his way up the front of the chair with his forelimbs. Just when one final backward heave would have seen the great dog ensconced on her lap, Mrs. Westby looked up.

"Oh really, Brandy, you are silly!" She put a hand on his rump and sent him slithering to the carpet, where he lay disconsolately, looking at her with liquid eyes.

"What was all that about?" I asked.

Mrs. Westby laughed. "Oh, it's these old jeans. When Brandy first came here as a tiny puppy, I spent hours holding him on my knee, and I used to wear the jeans a lot then. Ever since, the very sight of them makes him try to get on my knee, even though he knows perfectly well I can't have a huge Labrador in my lap."

"So now it's the stealthy approach, eh?"

She giggled. "That's right. Sometimes it works, when I'm pre-occupied—knitting or reading. If he's been playing in the mud, he makes an awful mess and I have to go and change. That's when he really gets a scolding!"

This patient of mine, Brandy, added color to my daily rounds. When I was walking my own dog, I often saw him playing in the fields by the river. One particularly hot day many of the dogs were taking to the water to cool off, but whereas they all glided in and swam off sedately, Brandy's approach was unique; he ran up to the riverbank, launched himself outward, legs splayed in a sort of swallow dive, and hung for a moment in the air rather like a flying fox before splashing thunderously into the depths. To me it was the action of a completely happy extrovert.

On the following day in those same fields I witnessed something even more extraordinary. There in a little playground Brandy was disporting himself on the slide. For this activity he had assumed an uncharacteristically grave expression and stood calmly in the queue of children. When his turn came he mounted the steps, slid down—all dignity and importance—then took a staid walk around to rejoin the queue.

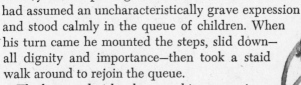

The boys and girls who were his companions seemed to take him for granted, but I found it difficult to tear myself away. I could have watched him all day.

I often smiled to myself when I thought of Brandy's antics, but I didn't smile when Mrs. Westby brought him into the surgery a few months later. His bounding ebullience had disap-peared, and he dragged himself along the passage to the con-sulting room.

As I lifted him onto the table, I noticed that he had

lost a lot of weight. "What's the trouble, Mrs. Westby?" I asked.

She looked at me worriedly. "He's been listless and coughing for a few days and not eating very well, but this morning he seems quite ill, and you can see he's starting to pant."

"Yes . . . yes. . . ." As I inserted the thermometer I watched the rapid rise and fall of the rib cage and noted the gaping mouth and anxious eyes. "He does look very sorry for himself."

His temperature was 104. I applied my stethoscope. I have heard of an old Scottish doctor describing a seriously ill patient's chest as sounding like a "kist o' whustles," and that just about described Brandy's. Rales, wheezes, squeaks and bubblings were all there against a background of labored respiration.

I put the stethoscope back in my pocket. "He's got pneumonia."

"Oh dear." Mrs. Westby reached out and touched the heaving chest. "That's bad, isn't it?"

"Yes, I'm afraid so."

"But . . ." She gave me an appealing glance. "I understand it isn't so fatal since the new drugs came out."

I hesitated. "In humans and most animals the sulfa drugs, and now penicillin, have changed the picture completely, but dogs are still very difficult to cure."

"You don't think it's hopeless?" Mrs. Westby asked.

"No, not at all. I'm just warning you that many dogs don't respond to treatment. But Brandy is young and strong and stands a fair chance. I wonder what started this off."

"I think I know, Mr. Herriot. He had a swim in the river about a week ago. I try to keep him out of the water in this cold weather, but if he sees a stick floating, he dives right in. You've seen him—it's one of the funny little things he does."

"Yes, I know. And was he shivery afterward?"

"He was. I walked him straight home, but it was such a freezing cold day. I could feel him trembling as I dried him down."

I nodded. "That would be the cause, all right. Anyway, let's start his treatment. I'm going to give him a penicillin injection, and I'll call at your house tomorrow to repeat it. He's not well enough to come to the surgery."

"Very well, Mr. Herriot. Is there anything else?"

"Yes. I want you to make him what we call a pneumonia jacket. Cut two holes in an old blanket for his forelegs and stitch him into it along his back—he must have his chest warmly covered."

I called and repeated the injection on the following day. There wasn't much change. I injected him for four more days, but Brandy wasn't responding. His temperature did drop a little; however, he ate hardly anything and gradually grew thinner. I put him on sulfapyridine tablets, but they didn't seem to help. As the days passed and he sank deeper into lethargy, I was forced to a conclusion that a few weeks before would have seemed impossible—this happy, bounding animal was going to die.

But Brandy didn't die. He survived, although you couldn't put it any higher than that. His temperature came down and his appetite improved, and he climbed onto a plateau of twilight existence where he seemed content to stay.

"He isn't Brandy anymore," Mrs. Westby said a few weeks later when I stopped by. Her eyes filled with tears as she spoke.

I shook my head. "No, I'm afraid he isn't. He has recovered from a really virulent pneumonia, but it's left him with a chronic pleurisy, adhesions and probably other lung damage."

She dabbed at her eyes. "It breaks my heart to see him like this. He's only five, but he's like an old, old dog. He was so full of life, too." She sniffed and blew her nose. "When I think of how I used to scold him for getting into the dustbin and muddying up my jeans. How I wish he would do some of his funny tricks now."

I thrust my hands deep into my pockets. "Never does anything like that anymore, eh?"

"No, he just hangs about the house. Doesn't even want to go for a walk."

As I watched, Brandy rose from his place in the corner and pottered over to the fire. He stood there a moment, gaunt and dead-eyed, before he coughed, groaned and flopped down on the hearthrug. Mrs. Westby was right; he *was* like a very old dog.

"Do you think he'll always be like this?" she asked.

I shrugged. "We can only hope not."

But as I got into my car and drove away, I really didn't have much hope. I had seen calves with lung damage after bad pneumonias. They recovered but were called "bad doers," because they remained thin and listless for the rest of their lives. Doctors, too, had plenty of "chesty" people on their books who were, more or less, in the same predicament.

Months went by, and the only time I saw the Labrador was when Mrs. Westby was walking him on his lead. I always had the impression that he was reluctant to move, and his mistress had to stroll along very slowly so that he could keep up with her. I sadly thought of the lolloping Brandy of old, but I told myself that at least I had saved his life. I could do no more for him now, and I made a determined effort to push him out of my mind.

I managed to do so fairly well until one afternoon in February. On the previous night I had treated a colicky horse until four a.m. and had just crawled into bed when I'd been called to a difficult calving. I'd got home too late to return to bed. Plowing through the morning rounds, I was so tired that I felt disembodied, and at lunch Helen watched me anxiously as my head nodded over my food.

There were a few dogs in the waiting room at two o'clock, and I peered at them through half-closed eyelids. By the time I reached my last patient, I was almost asleep on my feet. "Next, please," I mumbled as I pushed open the waiting-room door and stood back, expecting the usual sight of a dog being led out to the passage.

But this time there was a difference. There was a little poodle and a man in the doorway all right, but the thing that made my eyes snap wide open was that the dog was walking upright on his hind limbs.

Surely I wasn't seeing things? I stared down at the dog; the small creature strutted through the doorway, chest out, head up, as erect as a soldier.

His master must have seen my bewilderment, because he burst into laughter. "Don't worry, Mr. Herriot," he said. "This little dog was circus trained before I got him as a pet. I like to show off his little tricks. This one really startles people."

"You can say that again," I said.

The poodle wasn't ill; he just wanted his nails clipped. I smiled as I hoisted him onto the table and began to ply the clippers, but by the time I had finished, the lassitude had taken over again, and I felt ready to fall down as I showed man and dog out.

I watched the little animal trotting away down the street—in the orthodox manner this time—and it came to me suddenly that it had been a long time since I had seen a dog doing something unusual and amusing. Like the things Brandy used to do.

A wave of gentle memories flowed through me as I leaned wearily against the doorpost and closed my eyes. When I opened them, I saw Brandy coming around the corner with Mrs. Westby. His nose was entirely obscured by a large red tomato-soup can, and he strained madly at the leash and whipped his tail when he saw me.

It was certainly a hallucination this time. . . . I was looking into the past. . . . I really ought to go to bed immediately. But I was still rooted to the doorpost when the Labrador bounded up the steps and made an attempt, aborted by the soup can, to lick my face.

I stared into Mrs. Westby's radiant face. "What . . . what . . . ?"

With her sparkling eyes and wide smile she looked more attractive than ever. "Look, Mr. Herriot, he's better!"

In an instant I was wide-awake. "And I suppose you'll want me to get that can off him?"

"Oh yes, please!"

It took all my strength to lift him onto the table. He was heavier now than before his illness. I reached for the forceps and began to turn the jagged edges of the can outward from the nose and mouth. Tomato soup must have been one of his favorites, because he was really deeply embedded, and it took some time before I was able to slide the can from his face.

I fought off his slobbering attack. "He's back in the dustbin, I see."

"Yes, quite regularly. And he goes sliding with the children, too." She smiled happily.

I listened to his lungs; they were wonderfully clear. A slight roughness here and there, but the old cacophony had gone. I leaned on the table and looked at the great dog with a mixture of thankfulness and incredulity. He was as before, boisterous and full of the joy of living.

"But, Mr. Herriot." Mrs. Westby's eyes were wide. "How on earth has this happened? How has he got better?"

"*Vis medicatrix naturae,*" I replied in tones of deep respect. "The healing power of nature. Something no veterinary surgeon can compete with when it decides to act."

"I see. And you can never tell when this is going to happen?"

"No."

For a few seconds we were silent as we stroked the dog.

"Oh, by the way," I said. "Has he shown any renewed interest in the blue jeans?"

"Oh, my word, yes! They're in the washing machine at this very moment. Absolutely covered in mud. Isn't it marvelous!"

13

"*I let my heart fall into careless hands.*" Little Rosie's voice piped in my ear as I drove. I was on my way to dress a wound on a cow's back, and it was nice to hear the singing. When Jimmy had entered school, I missed his company on my rounds, the childish chatter that never palled, and the intense pleasure of seeing his growing wonder at the things of the countryside. Now it was all beginning anew with Rosie.

The singing had originated in the purchase of a radio phonograph. Music has always meant a lot to me and I already owned a record player, but I wanted better sound, and at that time there were no hi-fis or stereos—the best a music lover could do was to get a good phonograph. After much agonizing, reading of pamphlets and listening to advice, I decided to buy a Murphy—a handsome piece of furniture with a louvered front, which bellowed out the full volume of the Philharmonia Orchestra without a trace of muzziness. There was only one snag. It cost more than ninety pounds, and that was a lot of money in 1950.

"Helen," I said when it was installed, "the kids can use my old player, but we must keep them away from the Murphy."

Foolish words. The very next day as I came home, the passage was echoing with *"Yippee ay ooooh, yippee ay aaaay, ghost riders in the sky!"* It was the other side of Bing Crosby's "Careless Hands"—Rosie's favorite—and the Murphy was giving it full value.

I peeped into the sitting room as "Ghost Riders" came to an end. With her chubby little hands Rosie removed the record, placed it in its cover and marched, pigtails swinging, to the record cabinet. She had just selected another disc when I waylaid her.

"Which one is that?" I asked.

" 'The Little Gingerbread Man,' " she replied.

I looked at the label. It was, too, and how did she know? I had a whole array of these children's records—many of which looked exactly alike—and Rosie, now three, could not read.

She fitted the disc expertly on the turntable and set it going. When it was over, she picked out another record.

I looked over her shoulder. "What is it this time?"

" 'Tubby the Tuba.' " And indeed it was.

In the end I decided that it was fruitless to try to keep Rosie and the Murphy apart. Whenever she was not out with me, she played with the phonograph. It was her toy. It all turned out for the best, too, because she did my precious acquisition no harm, and during my rounds she sang, word perfect, the songs she had played so often. "Careless Hands" soon became my favorite, too.

There was a gate on the road to the farm we were visiting, and we came bumping up to it now. The singing stopped abruptly. This was one of my daughter's big moments. When I drew up, she jumped from the car, strutted proudly to the gate and opened it. She took this duty very seriously, and her small face was grave as I drove through. When she returned to take her place by my dog, Sam, on the seat, I patted her knee. "Thank you, sweetheart," I said. "You're a big help to me."

She blushed and swelled with importance. She knew I meant what I said, because opening gates is a chore.

We drove into the farmyard. The farmer, Mr. Binns, had shut the cow up in a ramshackle pen with a passage that stretched from a dead end to the outside. The animal in the pen was a Galloway—black and shaggy, with mean eyes—and I saw with some apprehension that her tail whipped perpetually, a sure sign of ill nature in a bovine.

"Couldn't you have got her tied up, Mr. Binns?" I asked.

The farmer shook his head. "Nay, I'm short o' room, and this un spends most of 'er time on the moors."

I could believe it. There was nothing domesticated about this animal. Usually I lifted my daughter into hayracks or onto the tops of walls while I worked, but I didn't want her anywhere near this beast. "It's no place for you in there, Rosie," I said. "Stand at the end of the passage, well out of the way."

Mr. Binns and I went into the pen, and I was pleasantly surprised when the farmer managed to drop a halter over the cow's head. He backed into a corner and held tightly to the shank.

I looked at him doubtfully. "Can you hold her?"

"I think so," Mr. Binns replied a little breathlessly. "You'll find t'place at the end of her back, there."

As I gently passed my fingers over the big abscess near the root of the animal's tail, the hind foot lashed out, catching me a glancing blow on the thigh. I had expected this, and I got on with my exploration. "How long has she had this?"

The farmer dug his heels in and leaned back on the rope. "Oh, 'bout two months. It keeps bustin' and fillin' up. Every time I thought it'd be the last, but it looks like it's never goin' to get right. What's t'cause of it?"

"I don't know, Mr. Binns. She must have had a wound there that became infected. On the back, drainage is poor. There's a lot of dead tissue I'll have to clear away before it can heal."

I leaned from the pen. "Rosie, will you bring my scissors, some cotton wool and that bottle of peroxide?"

The farmer watched wonderingly as the tiny figure trotted to the car and came back with the three things. "By gaw, t'little lass knows 'er way around."

"Oh yes," I said, smiling. "She's an expert on the things I use regularly." I reached over the door for the items, then Rosie retreated to her place at the end of the passage.

I began to work on the abscess. Since the tissue was dead, the cow couldn't feel a thing as I snipped and swabbed, but that didn't stop the hind leg from pistoning out every few seconds; this was one of those animals that just cannot tolerate any interference. I finished at last, then trickled some hydrogen peroxide over the area. I had a lot of faith in this old remedy as a penetrative antiseptic, and I watched contentedly as it bubbled on the skin. The cow, however, did not seem to enjoy the sensation, because she made a sudden leap into the air, tore the rope from the farmer's hands, brushed me to one side and made for the door. She crashed through it and into the passage. I desperately willed her to turn left, into the yard, but to my horror she thundered right, down toward the dead end where my daughter was standing.

It was one of the worst moments of my life. I heard a small voice say, "Mama." No scream, just that one word, said very quietly. Rosie was standing against the wall, and the cow, stationary now, was looking at her from a distance of two feet.

The animal turned when she heard my footsteps, then galloped past me into the yard. Overwhelmed with thankfulness, I lifted Rosie into my arms. She could easily have been killed.

As we started to drive away, I remembered that something very like this had happened when Jimmy was out with me. It had not been so horrific because he had been playing in a passage with an open end leading into a field, and he was not trapped when the cow I was working on broke loose and hurtled toward him. I could see nothing, but I heard a piercing yell of *"Aaaagh!"* before I rounded the corner. To my intense relief, Jimmy was streaking across the field to where my car was standing and the cow was trotting away in another direction.

This reaction had been typical because Jimmy was the noisy one of the family. Under stress he believed in making his feelings known in the form of loud cries. When Dr. Allinson came to give him his routine inoculations, for example, Jimmy heralded the appearance of the syringe with yells of *"Ow! This is going to hurt!"* And he had a kindred spirit in our good doctor, who bawled back at him, *"Aye. You're right, it is! Oooh! Aaah!"*

Now, as Rosie and I left the farm, she solemnly opened and closed the gate for me, then looked up at me expectantly. I knew why—she wanted to play one of her games. She loved being quizzed, just as Jimmy had loved to quiz me.

I took my cue and began. "Name six blue flowers."

She blushed quickly in satisfaction, because of course she knew. "Field scabiosa, harebell, forget-me-not, bluebell, speedwell, meadow cranesbill."

"Clever girl," I said. "Now—how about six birds?"

Again the blush and the quick reply. "Magpie, curlew, thrush, plover, yellowhammer, rook."

The game went on daily, with infinite variations. I only half realized then how lucky I was. I had my job and the company of my children at the same time. So many men work so hard to keep the home going that they lose touch with their families. But both Jimmy and Rosie, until they went to school, spent most of their time with me on the farms.

As Rosie's school days approached, her attitude, always solicitous, became distinctly maternal. "Daddy," she would say seriously, "how are you going to manage when I'm at school—all those gates to open and having to get everything out of the car yourself? It's going to be awful for you."

Patting her head, I used to try to reassure her. "I'm going to miss you, Rosie, but I'll get along somehow."

Her response was always the same: a relieved smile, and then the comforting words, "Never mind, Daddy. I'll be with you on Saturdays and Sundays. You'll be all right then."

I suppose it was natural that my children, seeing veterinary practice from early childhood and witnessing my pleasure in it, never thought of being anything but veterinary surgeons.

There was no problem with Jimmy; he was a tough little fellow, well able to stand the buffets of our job, but somehow I couldn't bear the idea of my daughter being kicked and knocked about and covered with muck. Practice was so much rougher in those days; there were no metal crushes to hold the big struggling beasts that regularly put vets in hospital with broken legs and ribs. I have always believed that children should follow their own inclinations, but as Rosie entered her teens, I dropped broad hints, and perhaps played unfairly by showing her as many grisly jobs as possible. She did finally decide to be a doctor on humans, and today she is "Dr. Rosie" in our community.

Now, when I see the high percentage of girls in veterinary schools and observe the excellent work done by the two women assistants in our own practice, I sometimes wonder if I did the right thing. But Rosie is happy and successful, and parents can only do what they think is right at the time.

However, all that was far in the future as I drove home from Mr. Binns's with my three-year-old daughter by my side. She had started to sing again and was just finishing the last verse of her great favorite: *"Careless hands don't care when dreams slip through."*

14

WAS there no peace in a vet's life? I wondered fretfully as I hurried my car along the road to Gilthorpe village. Eight o'clock on a Sunday evening and here I was, trailing off to visit a dog ten miles away; according to Helen, who had taken the message, the animal had been ailing for more than a week.

When I left Darrowby, the streets of the little town were empty in the gathering dusk and the houses had that tight-shut, comfortable look that raised images of armchairs and pipes and firesides; and now, as I saw the lights of the farms winking on the fells, I could picture the stockmen dozing contentedly with their feet up. I had not passed a single car on the darkening road. There was nobody out but Herriot.

I was sloshing around in a trough of self-pity by the time I drew up outside a row of gray stone cottages in Gilthorpe. "Mrs. Cundall, number 4, Chestnut Row," Helen had written on the slip of paper, and as I opened the gate and stepped through the tiny strip of garden, my mind was busy with half-formed ideas of what I was going to say. No need to be rude, just a firm statement of my position, that vets liked to relax on Sunday evenings just like other people, and though we did not mind coming out for emergencies, we did object to visiting animals that had been ill for a week.

I had my speech fairly well prepared when a little middle-aged woman opened the door.

"Good evening, Mrs. Cundall," I said, slightly tight-lipped.

"Oh, it's Mr. Herriot." She smiled shyly. "We've never met, but I've seen you walkin' round Darrowby. Come in."

The door opened straight into the tiny low-beamed living room, and I took in at a glance the shabby furniture and a curtained-off area at the end. Mrs. Cundall pulled the curtain aside. In a narrow bed lay a skeleton-thin man with sunken eyes in a yellowed face.

"This is my husband, Ron," she said cheerfully. The man smiled and raised a bony arm in greeting.

"And here is your patient, Hermann," she went on, pointing to a dachshund who sat by the side of the bed.

"Hermann?"

"Yes, we thought it was a good name for a German sausage dog." They both laughed.

"An excellent name," I said. "He looks like a Hermann."

The little animal gazed up at me, bright-eyed and welcoming. I bent down and stroked his glossy coat. "He looks healthy. What's the trouble?"

"Over the last week he's been goin' funny on 'is legs," Mrs. Cundall replied. "We weren't all that worried, but tonight he sort of flopped down and couldn't get up again."

"I see. I noticed he didn't seem keen to rise when I patted him." I put my hand under the dog's body and gently lifted him to his feet. "Come on, lad, let's see you walk."

As I encouraged him, he took a few hesitant steps, but his hind end swayed progressively and he soon sat down again. I did not like the look of this at all.

"It's his back, isn't it?" Mrs. Cundall said. "He's strong enough on 'is forelegs."

"That's ma trouble, too," Ron said in a soft husky voice, but he was smiling, and his wife fondly patted his arm.

I lifted the dog onto my knee. "Yes, the weakness is certainly in the back." I began to palpate the lumbar vertebrae, watching for any sign of pain.

"Has he hurt 'imself?" Mrs. Cundall asked. "Has somebody hit 'im? We don't usually let him out alone, but sometimes he sneaks through the garden gate."

"There's always the possibility of an injury," I said. "But more likely it's his disks."

"Disks?"

"Yes, little pads of cartilage and fibrous tissue between the vertebrae. In long-bodied dogs like Hermann, they sometimes protrude into the spinal canal and press on the cord."

Ron's husky voice came again from the bed. "What's 'is prospects, Mr. Herriot?"

That was the question with this syndrome—anything from complete recovery to incurable paralysis. "Very difficult to say," I replied. "I'll give him an injection and some tablets, and we'll see how it goes."

I injected an analgesic and some antibiotic and counted out some salicylate tablets—the best treatment of the day.

"Now then, Mr. Herriot." Mrs. Cundall smiled at me eagerly. "Ron has a bottle o' beer every night about this time. Would you like to join 'im?"

"Well, it's very kind of you, but I don't want to intrude. . . ."

"Oh, you're not. We're glad to see you."

She poured two glasses of brown ale, propped her husband up with pillows and sat down by the bed.

"We're from South Yorkshire, Mr. Herriot," she said.

I nodded. I had noticed the difference from the local accent.

"Aye, we came up here eight years ago, after Ron's accident."

"What was that?"

"I were a miner," Ron said. "Roof fell in on me. I got a broken back, crushed liver and a lot o' other internal injuries, but two of me mates were killed in the same fall, so ah'm lucky to be 'ere." He sipped his beer. "I've survived, but Doctor says I'll never walk no more."

"I'm terribly sorry."

"Nay, nay," the husky voice went on. "I count me blessings, and I've a lot to be thankful for. Ah suffer very little, and I've got t'best wife in the world."

Mrs. Cundall laughed. "Oh, listen to 'im. But I'm right glad we came to Gilthorpe. We used to spend all our holidays here in the Dales; we were great walkers, and it was lovely to get away from the smoke and the chimneys. The bedroom in our old house just looked out on a lot o' brick walls, but here Ron has this big window right by 'im and he can see for miles."

"Yes," I said. "This is a lovely situation." The village was perched on a high ridge and that window would command a view of the green slopes running down to the river and climbing high to the wildness of the moor on the other side. This sight had often beguiled me on my rounds. The grassy paths climbing among the airy tops beckoned to me. But they would beckon in vain to Ron Cundall.

"Gettin' Hermann was a good idea, too," he said. "Ah used to feel lonely when t'missus went out, but the little feller's made all the difference. You're never alone when you've got a dog."

I smiled. "How right you are. What is his age now?"

"He's six," Ron replied. "Right in the prime o' life, aren't you, old lad?" He let his arm fall by the bedside, and his hand fondled the sleek ears.

"That seems to be his favorite place—nearby you."

"Aye, it's a funny thing. T'missus walks and feeds 'im, but he's very faithful to me. I only have to reach down and he's there."

I had often seen this with disabled people: their pets stayed close by, as if to comfort and befriend them.

I finished my beer and got to my feet. Ron looked up at me. "Reckon I'll spin mine out a bit longer." He glanced at his half-full glass. "Ah used to shift more some nights when I went out wi' the lads, but you know, I enjoy this one bottle just as much. Strange how things turn out."

His wife bent over him, mock-scolding. "Yes, you've had to right your ways, haven't you?" and they both laughed.

I moved toward the door. "Well, thank you for the drink, Mrs. Cundall. I'll look in to see Hermann on Tuesday."

As I left I waved to the man in the bed, and his wife put her hand on my arm. "We're grateful to you for comin' on a Sunday night, Mr. Herriot. We felt awful about callin' you, but you un-

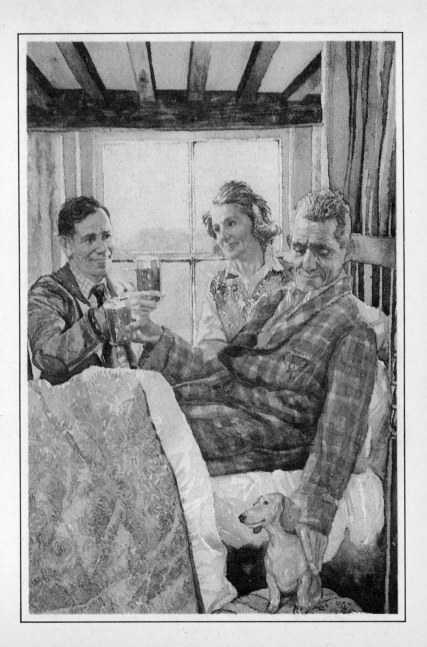

derstand it was only today that the little chap started going off his legs."

"Of course, please don't worry. I didn't mind in the least."

And as I drove through the darkness I knew that I didn't mind—now. My petty irritation had evaporated within minutes of entering that house, and I was left only with a feeling of humility. If that man back there had a lot to be thankful for, how about me? I had everything. I only wished I could dispel the foreboding I felt about his dog. There was a hint of doom about those symptoms of Hermann's, and yet I knew I just had to get him right. . . .

On Tuesday he looked a little worse.

"I think I'd better take him to the surgery for X ray," I said to Mrs. Cundall. "He doesn't seem to be improving."

In the car, Hermann curled up happily on Rosie's knee, submitting with good grace to her petting. And I had no need to anesthetize him when I placed him on our newly acquired X-ray machine. Those hindquarters stayed still all by themselves—too still for my liking.

In the pictures I thought I could detect a narrowing of the space between a couple of the vertebrae, which would confirm my suspicion of a disk protrusion. Today we can correct this condition with steroids or surgery, but in those days I could only continue my treatment, and hope.

By the end of the week hope had grown dim. I had supplemented the salicylates with other stimulant drugs, but Hermann was still unable to rise. I tweaked the toes of his hind limbs and was rewarded by a faint reflex movement, but I knew with a sick certainty that complete posterior paralysis was not far away.

By the next Saturday I had the unhappy experience of seeing my prognosis confirmed. When I entered the Cundalls' cottage, Hermann came to meet me, happy and welcoming in his front end but dragging his hind limbs helplessly.

"Hello, Mr. Herriot." Mrs. Cundall gave me a wan smile and looked down at the little creature stretched froglike on the carpet. "What d'you think of him now?"

I bent and tried the reflexes. Nothing. I shrugged my shoulders, unable to think of anything to reply. I looked at the gaunt figure in the bed. "Good morning, Ron," I said as cheerfully as I could, but his face was averted, looking out the window. It was as though he did not know I was there.

"Is he annoyed with me?" I whispered to his wife.

"No, no, it's this." She held out a newspaper. "It's upset him something awful." I looked at the printed page. On it was a large picture of a dachshund exactly like Hermann. This dog, too, was paralyzed, but its hind end was supported by a little four-wheeled trolley. The animal appeared to be sporting with its mistress and looked happy and normal, except for those wheels.

At the rustle of the newspaper Ron's head came around quickly. "What d'ye think of that, Mr. Herriot? D'ye agree with it?"

"Well . . . I don't know, Ron. I don't like the look of it, but I suppose that lady thought it was the only thing to do."

"Aye, maybe." The husky voice trembled. "But ah don't want Hermann to finish up like that." The arm dropped by the side of the bed and his fingers felt around on the carpet, but the little dog was still splayed out near the door. "It's 'opeless now, Mr. Herriot, isn't it?"

"Well, it was a black lookout from the beginning," I said. "These cases are so difficult. I'm sorry."

"Nay, I'm not blamin' you," he said. "You've done what ye could. What do we do now—put 'im down?"

"No, Ron, forget about that just now. Sometimes paralysis cases recover on their own after many weeks. We must carry on, for I honestly cannot say there is no hope."

On the way back to the surgery, the thought hammered in my brain. The hope I had extended was slight. Spontaneous recovery did sometimes occur, but Hermann's condition was extreme.

However, I kept going back every few days. Sometimes I took a couple of bottles of brown ale along in the evening and drank them with Ron. He and his wife were always cheerful, but the little dog never showed the slightest improvement. It was on one of these visits that I noticed an unpleasant smell as I entered the house. There was something familiar about it.

I sniffed, and the Cundalls looked at each other guiltily. Then

Ron spoke, his fingers twitching on the bedclothes. "It's some medicine ah've been givin' Hermann. Stinks like 'ell, but it's supposed to be good for dogs. Bill Noakes, an old mate o' mine—we used to work down t'pit together—put me on to it when he came to visit last weekend. Keeps a few whippets, does Bill. Knows a lot about dogs, and 'e sent me this stuff for Hermann."

Mrs. Cundall went to the cupboard and sheepishly presented me with a plain bottle. I removed the cork, and as the horrid stench rose up to me, my memory became suddenly clear. Asafetida, a common constituent of quack medicines before the war and still lingering on the shelves of occasional pharmacies. Its popularity was probably based on the assumption that anything that stank so badly must have magical properties. I knew it could not possibly do anything for Hermann.

I replaced the cork. "So you're giving him this, eh?"

Ron nodded. "Aye, three times a day. He doesn't like it much, but Bill says it's cured lots o' dogs with Hermann's problem." The deep-sunk eyes looked at me in silent appeal.

"Fine, Ron," I said. "Carry on. Let's hope it works." I knew the asafetida couldn't do any harm, and since my treatment had proved useless, I was in no position to turn haughty.

Mrs. Cundall smiled and Ron's expression relaxed. "That's grand, Mr. Herriot," he said. "Ah'm glad ye don't mind. I can dose the little feller myself. It's summat for me to do."

About a week later I called in at the Cundalls. "How are you today, Ron?" I asked.

"Champion, Mr. Herriot, champion." He always said that, but today there was a new eagerness in his face. He reached down and lifted his dog onto the bed. "Look 'ere." He pinched one hind foot, and there was a faint but definite retraction of the leg. I almost fell over in my haste to grab at the other foot. The result was the same.

"Look at that," I gasped. "The reflexes are coming back."

Ron laughed. "Bill Noakes's stuff's working, isn't it?"

A gush of emotions, mainly professional shame and wounded pride, welled in me, but it was only for a moment. "Yes, Ron," I replied. "No doubt about it."

He stared up at me. "Then Hermann's going to be all right?"

"Well, it's early yet, but that's the way it looks."

It was several weeks more before the dachshund was back to normal, and it was a fairly typical case of spontaneous recovery, with nothing whatever to do with the asafetida or, indeed, with my own efforts.

My final call at the cottage happened around the same time as my first visit—eight o'clock in the evening—and when Mrs. Cundall ushered me in, the little dog bounded joyously up to me before returning to his post by the bed.

"Well, that's a lovely sight," I said. "He can gallop like a racehorse now."

Ron dropped his hand down and stroked the sleek head. "Aye, isn't it grand? By heck, it's been a worryin' time."

"I just looked in to make sure all was well." I gave Hermann a farewell pat. "Well, I'll be going."

"Nay, nay," Ron said. "Don't rush off. Have a bottle o' beer before ye go."

I sat down by the bed and sipped my beer, and their faces glowed with friendliness. I marveled because my part in Hermann's salvation had been anything but heroic. In their eyes everything I had done must have seemed bumbling and ineffectual, and they must have been convinced that all would have been lost if Ron's old chum Bill Noakes had not stepped in and put things right. But though my ego had been bruised, I did not really care; I was witnessing a happy ending instead of a tragedy.

15

"PARENTS need nerves of steel"—those words that I heard years ago came to mind many times while Jimmy and Rosie were growing up. One notable occasion was a recital given by Miss Livingstone's piano class.

A soft-voiced, charming lady in her fifties, Miss Livingstone started many of the local children in piano lessons, and once a year she held a concert in the Methodist Hall for her pupils to show their paces. They ranged from six-year-olds to teenagers, and the room was packed with their proud parents. Jimmy was nine at the time and had been practicing without much enthusiasm for the big day.

Everybody knows everybody else in a small town like Darrowby, and as the place filled up, there was much nodding and smiling when people recognized each other. I found myself on the center aisle, with Helen on my right, and just across the way I saw Jeff Ward, old Willie Richardson's cowman, sitting very upright, dressed in his Sunday best.

"Hello, Jeff," I said. "One of your youngsters performing?"

He turned and grinned. "Aye, it's our Margaret. She's been comin' on right well at t'piano, and I just hope she does herself justice this afternoon."

"She will, Jeff. Miss Livingstone is an excellent teacher."

He nodded and turned to the front as the concert commenced. The first few performers who mounted the platform were very small boys in shorts and socks, or tiny girls in frilly dresses, and their feet dangled far above the pedals as they sat at the keyboard. Miss Livingstone hovered nearby to prompt them, but their little mistakes were greeted with indulgent smiles from the assembly, and the conclusion of each piece was greeted with thunderous applause.

I noticed, however, that as the children grew bigger and the pieces became more difficult, a certain tension began to build in the hall. The errors weren't so funny now, and when little Jenny Newcombe, the fruiterer's daughter, halted a couple of times, the silence in the room was absolute and charged with anxiety. When Jenny successfully restarted and I relaxed with all the others, the realization burst upon me that we were not just a roomful of parents watching our children perform; we were a band of brothers and sisters suffering together.

When little Margaret Ward climbed to the platform, her father stiffened perceptibly in his seat, his big, work-roughened fingers clutching tightly at his knees. However, Margaret went on very nicely till she came to a rather complicated chord that jarred with harsh dissonance. She knew she had got the notes wrong and tried again . . . and again . . . and again.

"No, C and E, dear," murmured Miss Livingstone, and Margaret crashed her fingers down once more, violently and wrongly.

She's not going to make it, I breathed to myself, aware that my pulse was racing and my muscles were rigid.

I glanced over at Jeff. His face had assumed a hideously mottled appearance and his legs were twitching convulsively. Just beyond him, his wife was leaning forward. Her mouth hung slightly open and her lips trembled.

It seemed an eternity before Margaret got the right notes and galloped through the rest of the piece, and although everybody applauded at the finish, the episode had taken its toll on all of us. I certainly didn't feel so good and watched in a half trance as a succession of children went up and played their pieces without incident. Then it was Jimmy's turn.

There was no doubt that most of the performers—as well as their parents—were suffering from nerves, but this couldn't be said of my son. He almost whistled as he trotted up the steps, and there was a hint of swagger in his walk over to the piano. In marked contrast, I found I was breathing with difficulty. My palms broke out in instant sweat.

Jimmy's piece was called "The Miller's Dance," a title burned on my brain till the day I die. It was a rollicking little melody, which of course I knew down to the last semiquaver, and Jimmy started off in great style, throwing his hands about and tossing his head like Artur Rubinstein in full flow.

Around the middle of "The Miller's Dance" there is a pause in the quick tempo where the music goes from a brisk ta-rum-tum-tiddle-iddle-om-pom-pom to a lingering taa-rum, taa-rum, before starting off again at top speed. It was a clever little ploy of the composer's and gave a touch of variety to the piece.

Jimmy dashed up to this point with flailing arms till he slowed down at the familiar taa-rum, taa-rum. I waited for him to take off again, but nothing happened. He stopped and looked down fixedly at the keys for a few seconds; then he played the slow bit again and halted once more.

My heart gave a great thud. Come on, lad, you know the next

part—I've heard you play it a hundred times. But Jimmy didn't seem troubled. He looked down with mild puzzlement and rubbed his chin.

Miss Livingstone's gentle voice came over the quivering silence. "Perhaps you'd better start at the beginning, Jimmy."

"Okay." My son's tone was perky as he plunged confidently into the melody again, and I closed my eyes as he approached the fateful bars. Ta-rum-tum-tiddle-iddle-om-pom-pom, taa-rum, taa-rum—then nothing. This time he put his hands on his knees and bent closely over the keyboard as though the strips of ivory were trying to hide something from him. He showed no panic, only a faint curiosity.

In the almost palpable hush of that room, I was sure the hammering of my heart must be audible. I could feel Helen's leg trembling against mine. I knew we couldn't take much more of this.

Miss Livingstone's voice was soft as a zephyr. "Jimmy, dear, shall we try it once more from the beginning?"

"Yes, yes, right." Away he went again like a hurricane, all fire and fury. It was unbelievable that there could ever be a flaw in such virtuosity.

By now the other parents had come to know "The Miller's Dance" almost as well as I did, and we waited in agony for the dread passage. Jimmy came up to it at breakneck speed. Ta-rum-tum-tiddle-iddle-om-pom-pom, then taa-rum, taa-rum . . . and silence. Helen's knees were definitely knocking now, and she was very pale.

As Jimmy sat motionless except for a thoughtful drumming of his fingers against the woodwork of the piano, I felt I was going to choke. I glared around me desperately, and I saw that Jeff Ward was also in a bad way. His face had gone all blotchy again and perspiration covered his forehead. Something had to break soon, and once more it was Miss Livingstone's voice that cut into the terrible atmosphere.

"All right, Jimmy, dear," she said. "Never mind. Perhaps you'd better go and sit down now."

My son rose from the stool and marched across the platform to rejoin his fellow pupils in the first few rows.

I slumped back in my seat. Ah well, that was it. The final indignity. The poor little lad had blown it. And though he didn't seem troubled, I was sure he must feel a sense of shame.

A wave of misery enveloped me, and though many of the other parents turned and directed sickly smiles of sympathy at Helen and me, it didn't help. I hardly heard the rest of the concert, which was a pity, because as the bigger boys and girls began to perform, the musical standard rose to remarkable heights, from Chopin nocturnes to Mozart sonatas. It was a truly splendid show—by everybody but poor old Jimmy, the only one who hadn't managed to finish.

At the end, Miss Livingstone came to the front of the platform. "Well, thank you, ladies and gentlemen, for your kind reception. I do hope you have enjoyed it as much as we have."

There was more clapping and the pushing back of chairs. But Miss Livingstone wasn't through. "Just one thing more, ladies and gentlemen." She raised a hand. "There is a young man here who, I know, can do much better. I wouldn't be happy going home now without giving him another opportunity. Jimmy." She beckoned toward the second row. "Jimmy, I wonder if you would like to have one more try."

As Helen and I exchanged horrified glances, our son's voice rang out, chirpy and confident. "Aye, I'll have a go!"

I couldn't believe it. The martyrdom was surely not about to start all over. But it was true. The small familiar figure was already striding to the piano. From a great distance I heard Miss Livingstone again. "Jimmy will play 'The Miller's Dance.'" She didn't have to tell us—we all knew.

A few seconds earlier I had been conscious only of a great weariness, but now I was gripped by a fiercer tension than I had known all afternoon. As Jimmy poised his hands over the keys, a vibrant sense of strain lapped around the silent room. The little lad started off as he always did, as though he hadn't a care in the world, and I began a series of long, shuddering breaths designed to carry me past the moment that was fast approaching. Because I knew that he would stop again. And I knew just as surely that when he did, I would topple senseless to the floor.

When he reached the crucial bars I closed my eyes tightly. But I could still hear the music—so very clearly. Ta-rum-tum-tiddle-iddle-om-pom-pom, taa-rum, taa-rum . . . There was a pause of unbearable length, then, tiddle-iddle-om-pom, tiddle-iddle-om-pom, Jimmy was blissfully on his way again.

He raced through the second half of the piece, but I kept my eyes closed as relief flooded through me, opening them only when he came to the finale. Jimmy was making a real meal of it, head down, fingers thumping, and at the last crashing chord he held up one hand in a flourish a foot above the keyboard before letting it fall by his side, like a true concert pianist.

I doubt if the Methodist Hall has ever heard a noise like the great cheer that followed. The place erupted in a storm of clapping and shouting, and Jimmy was not the man to ignore such an accolade. All the other children had walked impassively from the stage at the end of their efforts, but not so my son. To my astonishment, he strode to the front of the platform, placed one arm across his abdomen and the other behind his back, extended one foot and bowed, first to one side of the audience then to the other, with the grace of an eighteenth-century courtier.

The cheering changed to a great roar of laughter, which continued as he left the platform, and everybody was still giggling as we made our way out. In the doorway we bumped into Miss Mullion, who ran the little school that our son attended. "Oh dear," she said, dabbing at her eyes. "You can always depend on Jimmy to provide the light relief."

I drove back to Skeldale House slowly. I was still in a weakened condition, and I felt it dangerous to exceed twenty-five miles an hour. The color had returned to Helen's face, but there were lines of exhaustion around her mouth and eyes as she stared ahead through the windshield.

Jimmy, in the back, was lying full length along the seat, whistling some of the tunes that had been played that afternoon.

"Mum! Dad!" he exclaimed in the staccato manner so typical of him. "I like music."

I glanced at him in the driving mirror. "That's good, son. So do we."

Suddenly he rolled off the back seat and thrust his head be-tween us. "Do you know why I like music so much?"

I shook my head.

"Because it's"—he groped rapturously for the phrase—"because it's so soothing."

16

WHEN Walt Barnett asked me to see his cat, I was surprised. He had always employed other veterinary surgeons, ever since Sieg-fried had mortally offended him by charging him ten pounds for castrating a horse, and that had been a long time ago. I was sur-prised, too, that a man like him should concern himself with the ailments of a cat.

Walt Barnett was reputed to be the richest man in Darrowby. He was mainly a scrap merchant, but he had a haulage business, too. In fact, he did anything that came his way, if there was money in it—for money was the ruling passion of his life. There was no profit in cat keeping.

Another thing that puzzled me as I drove to his office was that owning a pet indicated some warmth of character, a vein of senti-ment, however small. It just didn't fit into his nature.

I picked my way through the scrapyard to the shed from which the empire was run. Walt Barnett was sitting behind a cheap desk exactly as I remembered him, the massive body stretching the seams of the shiny navy-blue suit, and the brown trilby hat perched on the back of his head. Unchanged, too, was the beefy red face with its arrogant expression and hostile eyes.

"Over there," he said, glowering at me and poking a finger at a black and white cat sitting among the papers on the desk.

It was a typical greeting. I hadn't expected him to say good morning, and he never smiled. I reached across the desk to tickle the animal's cheek and was rewarded by a rich purring. He was a big tom, long-haired and attractively marked, with a white breast and white paws, and I took an immediate liking to him.

"Nice cat," I said. "What's the trouble?"

"It's 'is leg there. Must've cut 'isself."

I felt among the fluffy hair, and the little creature flinched as I reached a point halfway up the limb. I took out my scissors and clipped a clear area. I could see a deep transverse wound with a thin serous discharge. "Yes . . . this could be a cut. But there's something unusual about it. I can't see how he's done it. Does he go out in the yard much?"

The big man nodded. "Aye, wanders around a bit."

"Ah well, he may have caught it on some sharp object. I'll give him a penicillin injection and leave you a tube of ointment to squeeze into the wound morning and night."

Some cats object strongly to hypodermics, and since their armory includes claws as well as teeth, they can be difficult, but this one never moved as I inserted the needle. In fact, the purring increased.

"He really is good-natured," I said. "What do you call him?"

"Fred." Walt Barnett looked at me expressionlessly, discouraging further comment.

I produced the ointment from my bag and placed it on the desk. "Right, let me know if he doesn't improve."

I received no reply and took my leave, feeling the prickle of resentment that had heretofore characterized my dealings with this man. But as I walked across the yard, I soon forgot my annoyance in my preoccupation with the case. There was something peculiar about that wound. It didn't look accidental; it was neat and deep, as though somebody had drawn a razor blade across the flesh.

A touch on my arm brought me out of my musings. One of the men who had been working amid the scrap was looking at me conspiratorially. "You've been in to see t'big boss?"

"Yes."

"Funny thing, t'awd sourface botherin' about a cat, eh?"

"I suppose so. How long has he had it?"

"Oh, about two years now. It was a stray. Ran into 'is office one day, and, knowin' him, I thought he'd 'ave booted it straight out, but 'e didn't. Adopted it instead. Ah can't reckon it up. It sits there all day on 'is desk."

"He must like it," I said.

"Him? He doesn't like anythin' or anybody. He's a—"

A bellow from the office doorway cut him short. "Hey, you! Get on with your work!" Walt Barnett, huge and menacing, brandished a fist, and the man, terrified, scuttled away.

As I got into my car, the thought stayed with me that this was how Walt Barnett lived—surrounded by hate. His ruthlessness was a byword in the town, and though no doubt it had made him rich, I didn't envy him.

Two days later he telephoned. "Get out 'ere sharpish and see that cat."

"Isn't the wound any better?"

"Naw, it's wuss, so don't be long."

Fred was in his usual place on the desk, and he purred as I went up and stroked him, but the leg was certainly more painful. Even more baffling, the wound had lengthened; it was as though it were trying to creep its way around the leg.

I passed a metal probe gently into the depths of the cut. I could feel something there, something that caught the end of the probe and sprang away. I gripped the unknown object with forceps, and when I brought it to the surface and saw the narrow brown strand, all became suddenly clear.

"He's got an elastic band round his leg," I said. I snipped the thing off and dropped it on the desk. "There it is. He'll be all right now."

Walt Barnett jerked himself upright in his chair. "Elastic band! Why the 'ell didn't you find it fust time?"

"I'm sorry, Mr. Barnett," I said. "It was embedded in the flesh, out of sight."

"Well, 'ow did it get there?"

"Somebody put it on his leg, without a doubt."

"Put it on . . . Wot for?"

"Oh, there are some cruel folk around."

"One o' them fellers in the yard, ah'll wager."

"Not necessarily. Fred goes out in the street, doesn't he?"

"Oh aye, often."

"Well, it could have been anybody."

The big man scowled, eyes half closed. I wondered if he were going over the list of his enemies. That would take some time.

"Anyway," I said. "The leg will heal quickly now. That's the main thing."

Walt Barnett reached across the desk and slowly rubbed the cat's side with a sausagelike forefinger. I had seen him do this several times during my previous visit. It was an odd gesture but probably the nearest he could get to a caress.

On my way back to the surgery I slumped low in the car seat, hardly daring to think of what would have happened if I hadn't found that elastic. Arrest of circulation, gangrene, loss of the foot or even death. I broke into a sweat at the thought.

Walt Barnett was on the phone three weeks later, and I felt a twinge of apprehension at the sound of his voice.

"Is Fred's leg still troubling him?" I asked.

"Naw, that's 'ealed. There's summat matter with 'is head."

"His head?"

"Aye, keeps cockin' it from side to side. Come and see 'im."

The symptoms sounded like canker, and when I saw the cat, twisting his head around uneasily, I was sure that was it; but the ears were clean and painless. This amiable cat seemed to like being examined, and the purring rose to a crescendo as I inspected his teeth, mouth, eyes and nostrils. Nothing. Yet something up there was causing a lot of discomfort.

I began to work my way through the black hair on his neck, and suddenly the purring was interrupted by a sharp meow as my fingers came upon a painful spot.

"Something here," I murmured. I took out my scissors and began to clip. And as the hair fell away and the skin showed through, a wave of disbelief swept through me. I was looking down at a neat little transverse slit, a twin of the one I had seen before. But surely not on the neck!

I went into the wound with probe and forceps, and within seconds I had brought the familiar brown band to the surface and snipped it off. "Another elastic band," I said. "Somebody really meant business this time."

Walt Barnett drew his forefinger along the cat's furry flank. "Who could be doin' this?" he asked.

I shrugged. "No way of telling. The police are always on the lookout for cruelty, but they would have to catch a person actually in the act."

I knew he was wondering when the next attempt would come, and so was I, but there were no more elastic bands for Fred. The neck healed rapidly, and I didn't see the cat for nearly a year. Then Helen met me one morning as I was coming in from my rounds. "Mr. Barnett's just been on the phone, Jim. Would you please go at once? He thinks his cat has been poisoned."

I found a vastly different Fred this time. The cat was not on the desk but rather was crouched on the floor among a litter of newspapers. He retched and vomited a yellow fluid as I went over to him. More vomit lay around among pools of diarrhea with the same yellowish hue.

Walt Barnett spoke up. "He's poisoned, isn't 'e? Somebody's given 'im summat."

"It's possible. . . ." I watched the cat move slowly to a saucer of milk and sit over it in the same crouching attitude. He did not drink but sat looking down with a curious immobility. There was a sad familiarity in the little animal's appearance. This could be something worse even than poison.

"Well, it is, isn't it?" the big man went on. "Somebody's tried to kill 'im again."

"I'm not sure." As I took the cat's temperature, there was none of the purring of before. He was sunk in a profound lethargy. The temperature was 105 degrees. Palpating the abdomen, I felt a doughy consistency in the bowels, a lack of muscular tone.

"Well, if it's not that, what is it?"

"It's feline enteritis," I said. "Some people call it cat distemper. There's an outbreak in Darrowby just now. I've seen several cases lately, and Fred's symptoms are typical."

The big man heaved his bulk from behind the desk, went over to the cat and rubbed his forefinger along the unheeding back. "Can you cure 'im?"

"I'll do my best, but the mortality rate is very high."

"You mean, most of 'em die?"

"I'm afraid so."

"How can that be? I thought you fellers had all them wonderful new medicines now."

"This is a virus, and viruses are resistant to antibiotics."

"Awright, then. What are you goin' to do?"

"I'm going to start right now," I said. I injected electrolytic fluid to combat the dehydration. I gave antibiotics against the secondary bacteria and finished with a sedative to control the vomiting. But I knew that everything I had done was merely supportive. I had never had much luck with feline enteritis.

I visited Fred each morning, and the very sight of him made me unhappy. He was either hunched over the saucer or curled up on the desk in a little basket. He had no interest in the world around him. When I gave him his injections it was like pushing a needle into a lifeless animal, and on the fourth morning I could see that he was sinking rapidly.

"I'll come by tomorrow," I said, and Walt Barnett nodded silently. He had shown no emotion throughout the cat's illness.

Next day, when I entered the office, I found the usual scene—Mr. Barnett in his chair, the cat in the basket on the desk.

Fred was very still, and as I approached I saw with a dull feeling of inevitability that he was not breathing. I put my stethoscope over his heart, then looked up.

"I'm afraid he's dead, Mr. Barnett."

The big man did not change expression. He reached slowly across and rubbed his forefinger against the dark fur in that familiar gesture. Then he put his elbows on the desk and covered his face with his hands. I watched helplessly as his shoulders began to shake and tears welled between the thick fingers. He stayed like that for some time, then he spoke. "He was my friend."

I could find no words, and the silence was heavy in the room until he suddenly pulled his hands from his face and glared at me defiantly. "Aye, ah know what you're thinkin'. This is that big tough Walt Barnett, cryin' his eyes out over a cat. What a joke! I reckon you'll have a bloody good laugh later on."

He was sure that what he considered a display of weakness would lower my opinion of him, and yet he was so wrong. I have liked him better ever since.

17

It was a Sunday morning in June, and I was washing my hands in the sink in Matt Clarke's kitchen. The sun was bright, and there was a brisk wind scouring the fellsides; through the window I could see every cleft and gully lying sharp and clear on the green flanks as the cloud shadows drove across them.

I glanced at the white head of Grandma Clarke bent over her knitting. The radio on the dresser was tuned to the morning service, and as I watched, the old lady looked up from her work and listened intently to some words of the sermon before starting her needles clicking again.

In that brief time I had a profound impression of serenity and unquestioning faith that has remained with me to this day. Whenever I have heard discussions and arguments on the varying religious beliefs and doctrines, there still rise before me the seamed old face and calm eyes of Grandma Clarke. She knew and was secure. Goodness seemed to flow from her.

She was in her late eighties and always dressed in black with a little black neckband. She had come through the hard times of farming and could look back on a long life of toil, in the fields as well as in the home.

As I reached for the towel, Matt led Rosie into the kitchen. "Mr. Clarke has been showing me some baby chicks, Daddy," Rosie said.

Grandma looked up. "Is that your lass, Mr. Herriot?"

"Yes, Mrs. Clarke," I replied. "This is Rosie."

"Aye, of course. I've seen her before, many a time." The old lady put down her knitting and rose stiffly from her chair. She shuffled over to a cupboard, brought out a gaily colored tin and extracted a bar of chocolate. "How old are ye now, Rosie?" she asked as she presented the sweet.

"Thank you. I'm six," my daughter replied.

Grandma looked down at the smiling face, at the sturdy, tanned legs in their blue shorts and sandals. "Well, you're a grand little lass." For a moment she rested her work-roughened hand against the little girl's cheek, then she returned to her chair. They didn't make much of a fuss, those old Yorkshire folk, but to me the gesture was like a benediction.

The old lady picked up her knitting again. "And how's that lad o' yours? How's Jimmy?"

"Oh, he's fine, thank you. Ten years old now. He's out with some of his pals this morning."

"Ten, eh? Ten and six . . ." For a few seconds her thoughts seemed far away as she plied her needles, then she looked at me again. "Maybe ye don't know it, Mr. Herriot, but this is the best time of your life. When your children are young and growin' up around ye—that's when it's best. It's the same for everybody, only a lot o' folk don't know it and a lot find out when it's too late. It doesn't last long, you know."

"I believe I've always realized that, Mrs. Clarke, without thinking about it very much."

"Reckon you have, young man." She gave me a sideways smile. "You allus seem to have one or t'other of your bairns with you on your calls."

As I drove away from the farm, the old lady's words stayed in my mind; and they are still in my mind, all these years later, when Helen and I are about to celebrate forty years of marriage. Life has been and is still good to us—we have had so many wonderful times—but I think we both agree that Grandma Clarke was right about the very best time of all.

When I got back to Skeldale House that summer morning, I found Siegfried replenishing the store of drugs in his car trunk. His children, Alan and Janet, were helping. Like me, he usually took his family around with him.

He banged down the lid of the trunk. "Right, that's that for another few days." He glanced at me and smiled. "There are no more calls at the moment, James. Let's have a walk down the back."

With the children running happily ahead of us, we went through the passage and out into the long garden behind the house. Here the sunshine was imprisoned between the high old walls, with the wind banished to the upper air and ruffling the top leaves of the apple trees. When we reached the big lawn, Siegfried flopped on the turf and rested on his elbow. I sat down by his side.

My partner pulled a piece of grass and chewed it contemplatively. "Pity about the acacia," he murmured.

I looked at him in surprise. It was many years since the beautiful tree, which had once soared from the middle of the lawn, had blown down in a gale.

"Yes, it is," I said. "It was magnificent." I paused for a moment. "Remember, I fell asleep against it the day I came here to apply for a job? We first met right on this spot."

Siegfried laughed. "I do remember." He looked around him at the mellow brick and stone copings of the walls, at the rockery and rose bed, at the children playing in the old hen house at the far end. "My word, James, when you think about it, we've come through a few things together since then. A lot of water, as they say, has flowed under the bridge."

We were both silent for a while, and my thoughts went back over the struggles and the laughter of those years. I lay back on the grass and closed my eyes, feeling the sun warm on my face, hearing the hum of the bees among the flowers, the croaking of the rooks in the great elms that overhung the yard.

My colleague's voice seemed to come from afar. "Hey, you're not going to do the same trick again, are you? Going to sleep in front of me?"

I sat up, blinking. "Gosh, I'm sorry, Siegfried, I nearly did. I was out at a farrowing at five o'clock this morning and it's just catching up with me."

"Ah well. You won't need to read yourself to sleep tonight."

Siegfried and I each had favorite books to which we sometimes resorted when sleep would not come—books that never failed to start us nodding. I laughed. "No," I said, rubbing my eyes. "I won't need any encouragement tonight." I rolled onto my side. "By the way, I was at Matt Clarke's this morning." I told him what Grandma had said.

Siegfried selected a fresh piece of grass and resumed his chewing. "Well, she's a wise old lady and she's seen it all." My partner startled me then by sitting up abruptly. "Do you know, James," he said, "I'm convinced that the same thing applies to our job. We're going through the best time there, too."

"Do you think so?"

"Sure of it. Look at all the new advances since the war—drugs and procedures we never dreamed of. We can look after our animals in a way that would have been impossible a few years ago, and the farmers realize this. You've seen them crowding into the surgery on market day to ask advice—they've gained respect for the profession and they know it pays to call in the vet now."

"That's true," I said. "We're certainly busier than ever."

"In fact, James, I'd like to bet that these present years are the high noon of country practice."

I thought for a moment. "You could be right. But if we are on the top now, does it mean that our lives will decline later?"

"No, no, of course not. They'll be different, that's all. I sometimes think we've only touched the fringe of so many things. . . ." Siegfried brandished his gnawed piece of grass at me, and his eyes shone with the enthusiasm that always uplifted me.

"I tell you this, James. There are great days ahead!"

Still "Our Vet"

"Mr. Herriot," said a Yorkshire taxi driver to a visiting journalist, "he tends my dog. A nice man, a bit quiet."

In spite of the fame that James Herriot's books have brought him, his life remains essentially unchanged. First and foremost he is still a country vet, absorbed in his practice. Although he has always taken pains to disguise the true identity of his fictional town of Darrowby, forty to fifty fans turn up every day on his doorstep; but the animals in the surgery are always tended first. Only then does Herriot go out to meet his reading public, to pose for their clicking cameras and to autograph his books.

James Herriot

James and Helen now live in a village outside "Darrowby." The practice has increased in size. Siegfried and James have been joined by James's son, Jimmy, and in addition to three veterinary assistants, they also have the help of Jimmy's own five-year-old son, Nicholas. In true Herriot tradition, he loves to accompany his father on his rounds, but whether Nicholas' baby sister, Zoe, will also join the practice is still in doubt. Herriot's daughter, Rosie, meanwhile, is a people doctor in a nearby group practice; her seven-year-old daughter, Emma, is the third of James and Helen's grandchildren.

In the past, James traveled widely in connection with veterinary work and to publicize his books, but these days he prefers to stay at home. When a new book comes out, he tours the British Isles for signing sessions and much enjoys meeting his readers. But the Herriots' idea of a perfect holiday is to tuck themselves away in a remote little cottage they have in the Dales.

Although James Herriot has been in practice since before World War II, he has not begun to think of retirement. "I just can't imagine what it would be like never to go through that surgery door again," he says. "I'm too fond of animals."

ACKNOWLEDGMENTS

Page 79, lines 31-32: from the song "Little Girls" in the musical *Annie*, lyric by Martin Charnin, music by Charles Strouse, © 1977 by Edwin H. Morris & Company, A Division of MPL Communications, Inc., and Charles Strouse. International copyright secured. All rights reserved. Used by permission.

Page 230, line 18; 235, lines 11-12: from the song "Careless Hands," words and music by Bob Hilliard and Carl Sigman. Copyright 1949 by Edwin H. Morris & Company, A Division of MPL Communications, Inc., © renewed 1976 by Better-Half Music Co., © renewed 1977 by Edwin H. Morris & Company, A Division of MPL Communications, Inc. International copyright secured. Used by permission.

Page 231, lines 1-2: from the song "(Ghost) Riders in the Sky," words and music by Stan Jones, copyright 1949 by Edwin H. Morris & Company, A Division of MPL Communications, Inc., © renewed 1977 by Edwin H. Morris & Company, A Division of MPL Communications, Inc. International copyright secured. All rights reserved. Used by permission.